THE LIFE AND TIMES OF
DR WILLIAM MACKENZIE

THE
LIFE AND TIMES OF
DR WILLIAM MACKENZIE

Founder of the

Glasgow Eye Infirmary

BY

A. M. WRIGHT THOMSON

T.D., M.D., F.R.C.P. Glasg., D.O.M.S.

Consultant Ophthalmologist, Glasgow Eye Infirmary and Gartnavel General
Hospital, Royal Beatson Memorial Hospital, Bridge of Weir Hospital
and Quarrier's Home, Bridge of Weir.

Privately printed by
ROBERT MACLEHOSE AND COMPANY LIMITED
THE UNIVERSITY PRESS, GLASGOW
1973

This book is dedicated to all who have in any way assisted in the work of the Glasgow Eye Infirmary over the past century and a half and especially to those members of the staff of all categories who, by their prompt action and devotion to duty, preserved the patients under their care from harm during the disastrous fire of 17th January, 1971.

Contents

List of Illustrations

Introduction and Acknowledgments

IN 1974 the Glasgow Eye Infirmary will celebrate the 150th anniversary of its foundation and it seems appropriate to mark the occasion with the story of the man who was responsible for its beginnings.

Much water has flown under many bridges since 1824 and medical knowledge has increased out of all recognition. William Mackenzie was one who contributed much to the spread of this knowledge and it has been a most interesting study trying to find out how he lived, how he was trained and what he did.

Fortunately, he was careful to preserve a large number of letters and two diaries, one of his Continental journey and one of his stay in London. All these are preserved in the Library of the Royal College of Physicians and Surgeons of Glasgow and much of the research was done there accordingly. My thanks are due to the staff there and particularly to Miss Elizabeth Wilson whose help and enthusiasm proved invaluable indeed.

Further research was done in the Glasgow room of the Mitchell Library and I am grateful for help here also. The Glasgow University Library has in its possession testimonials which William Mackenzie submitted to the University in 1833 and I am grateful for permission to study these.

It would not be possible to detail all the books and articles consulted, but prominent amongst them was the late Dr John Marshall's address entitled 'William Mackenzie, the making of an Ophthalmologist', delivered on the occasion of the presentation of the Mackenzie medal to him in 1953.

All four of the British editions of Mackenzie's *Treatise* and most of the foreign ones are in the Library of the Glasgow Eye Infirmary and were available there. Old numbers of the *British Journal of Ophthalmology* and the *Glasgow Medical Journal* were freely consulted.

The work has been supported by very generous grants from two bodies, the Board of Management for Glasgow Western and Gartnavel Hospitals and the Marc Fitch Fund, Chichester, Sussex. To both, I should like to tender my sincere thanks.

Three ladies have been most helpful; the Misses Lochhead, grand-nieces of Dr William Brown, William Mackenzie's partner, who presented a set of surgical instruments, purchased in Vienna in 1830, and several old photographs and documents to the Glasgow Eye Infirmary, and Mrs Webster, grand-niece of Mrs William Mackenzie who supplied some old pictures of her grand-uncle and aunt and other items.

Mr A. R. Forrester, a grand-nephew of Mrs Mackenzie by marriage, also provided some old documents.

The Scots Ancestry Research Society, Edinburgh, provided very helpful details from old Glasgow Parish Registers and other information which must have taken a long time to collect.

The pictures of Mr and Mrs William Napier, of William Mackenzie in later life and of Mrs Mackenzie were copied and improved by Messrs T. & R. Annan of West Campbell Street, Glasgow.

Part of the research involved reading passages in Latin and Greek and I was glad to call on the help of my brother, Ian, whose knowledge of the Classics is much greater than mine.

The typing of the manuscript was undertaken by the late Miss Elizabeth Stewart and Mrs Nan F. Thomson, my present Secretary. Both ladies worked very hard at the task which must have been irksome at times.

The Assistant Registrar in the Royal Archives at Windsor Castle, Mr E. H. Cuthbert, kindly supplied details of the Surgeon Oculists to the Sovereign in Scotland: Professor Arnold Sorsby supplied details of the foundation of the Royal Eye Hospital in London: Professor Ralph Pugh of London University assisted with much good advice on publication.

To all these good people go my sincere thanks for assisting in what has been a very enjoyable piece of research.

16 Kirklee Road
Glasgow G12

CHAPTER 1

Prelude: The Eighteenth-Century Quacks

WILLIAM MACKENZIE lived from 1791 until 1868, a period of great expansion in the British Isles. His native Glasgow grew from a cathedral and university town to a mighty industrial city during his life-time and the prosperity of the whole United Kingdom, thanks to the Industrial Revolution, became legendary. The practice of medicine was also revolutionised during his life-time and it is profitable to survey the scene before his arrival.

In the eighteenth century the art of healing was anything but scientific and was very much inclined to be empyrical. There was very little known about Ophthalmology in those days and some of the best-known quacks were so-called oculists. Three of them, William Read, Roger Grant and the Chevalier Taylor, gained great distinction, far beyond their deserts and all were patronised by royalty. They made huge fortunes in the course of their work, but they also made many enemies and the orthodox medical practitioners were often acutely embarrassed by them.

William Read was in practice at the end of the seventeenth century as an oculist and made the extraordinary statement in the *Tatler* in 1695 that he had been couching for thirty-five years, taking off wens, and curing wry-necks and hare-lips without blemish.

He was reputed to be illiterate and was a tailor to trade. His admirers did not appear to hold his lack of learning against him, but on the contrary a poem was addressed to him in 1705 congratulating him on his appointment as oculist to Queen Anne and criticising his detractors for pointing out that he was a man of little learning and making the point that his achievements were all the greater considering that he made himself master of so much true knowledge by a natural genius and application, without the help of their learned leading-strings.

He was knighted in 1707 for his services to a large number of soldiers and sailors whose sight was affected in the campaigns of the Duke of Marlborough in the War of the Spanish Succession.

His appointment as oculist to Queen Anne was the result of the Queen's myopia and, when he died in 1715, she appointed Roger Grant, a former tinker, to be her oculist. An epigram was composed at the time.

> Her Majesty sure was in a surprise
> Or else was very short-sighted,

When a tinker was sworn to look after her eyes
And the Mountebank Reed was knighted.

Read wrote several books which were of no real value, but the first one, written in 1706 and sold at 2/6d by Baker at the Black-Boy in Paternoster Row, had the grandiose title *A Short, but Exact Account of all the Diseases incident to the Eyes with the Causes, Symptoms and Cures also Practical Observations upon some Extraordinary Diseases of the Eyes.* It is almost mediaeval in its suggestions for treatment. For example, he denies the virtue of the white part of hen's dung as an application for diseases of the eye. It must be assumed that this had already been suggested as a form of therapy and takes its place beside dead men's skulls and foxes' dung which were also fashionable cures at that time.

He had the effrontery to entitle the first chapter 'Some errors Committed by the pretended Practitioners for the Eyes'. In this he recommends alum, copperis, salt, sandiver, juice of agrimony, celandine, dazy roots and houseleek. He also states that fretting upon the cornea with an eyespoon like a grater is good if properly used and that drawing and cutting grass through the eye and smoothing with a gold ring, cutting or scraping upon the cornea, will heal wounds, but never scars.

There is also a chapter on anatomy which describes the rampiers and defences, the coats, muscles, nerves, arteries, humours and kernals, commonly called glandules of the eye.

He gives over 120 pages to a description of the diseases of the eye. As a cause of proptosis, he suggests *inter alia* 'Great blowings in horns and trumpets' in the case of musicians.

As a cause of squint, he suggests keeping too much company with women, 'the excess whereof strangely dissipates the spirits; most commonly this distemper is most incident unto children, presently after their birth, through the negligence of their nurses who set the cradle in which the infant lyeth, sideways to the light and not directly contrary to it, which maketh the children looking towards the light, to turn the eye on that side towards it, and thus by continuance, they are accustomed to turn the eye away, till the muscles have contracted a habit.'

His treatment, where there is repletion or palsey of a muscle was to purge the brain by chewing things in the mouth, by putting sternutatories in the nose, by using a good diet and by strengthening the part with drying and resolving fomentations. He also recommends asses' milk, moist fomentations and pigeons' blood dropped into the eye.

He quotes Paulus Aegineta as using a mask for young children so that they may look straight ahead and also the use by older writers of something red fastened to the temples and on the contrary ear to the turning awry of the eye and the setting of the cradle with the contrary side to the light.

It is true to say, therefore, that there was in very early days a rudimentary knowledge of training for the cure of squints although often for the wrong reasons.

There is also a chapter on lice in the eyelids and he quotes a case occuring in the Guise family who was treated in France by the removal of worms and nits by a silver needle.

Read had an advertisement published entitled *Post Nubila Phoebus, Nihil Absque Deo* (After the clouds, sunlight. Nothing without God).

This included a large picture of a patient being treated, but also a coat of arms. The wording of the advertisement is hardly modest and states that he has been invited by some persons of considerable quality to perform some considerable cures such as couching for cataract and cancers, which he frequently performed without cutting.

'As many hundreds in England, Scotland and Ireland can sufficiently demonstrate. . . . He hath a Testimonial from the Vice-Chancellor, for several considerable cures he hath performed in the aforesaid University of Oxford. . . . which is a confirmation that he is none of those many Circumforaneous Pretenders that infest this Kingdom. . . . He likewise infallibly cures all pains in the Head, that very often occaions the Gutta Serena or Black Cataract, which are never cured, but means may be used in time that may prevent these Obstructions in the Optick Nerves that occasion them.'

There then follows a long list of patients, whose names are given, who had their sight restored, their cancers removed, or their wry-necks straightened. He also cut off a 'mortified legge in half-a-minute without the loss of an ounce of blood after the Styptick-Water was applied'; in the presence of His Grace the Duke of Northumberland. He cured a woman of a dead palsie and convulsions in the nerves after being eleven years bedridden and restored her to perfect use of her limbs, a double hare-lip was cut and cured by him in five days.

Sir William Read died in May 1715 at Rochester in Kent and was buried in St Nicholas Church there. Unfortunately, he left no Will and it cannot be learned how great a fortune he made, but if his achievements were anything like those listed above, he should have been very rich indeed.

He bore arms, but these were generally considered to be not his own, but belonging to the Read family of Llanndinan, Co. Montogmery.

Queen Anne appears to have had two oculists, since it is recorded that Roger Grant was appointed Oculist and Operator in Ordinary to Her Majesty in 1710. When Sir William Read died, he held the same post under George I. Although he was said to be a tinker, he was designated a cobbler by his kinder associates. He was a powerful anabaptist preacher and was reputed to have used his influence over his hearers to foster a belief in his semi-miraculous powers of healing. He practised in Mouse Alley, Wapping, and advertised twice a week in the *British Apollo*. He had another address at St Christopher's Churchyard, Threadneedle Street and appears to have practised at both addresses concurrently. His advertisements consisted of long lists of patients whom he had cured. These lists not only gave the patients' names, but also their addresses. One case he describes was a Mr Thomas Prosar who had one eye 'Couched by a great Pretender'. This eye, however, 'Perished in his head'. Mr Grant discovered him one day begging for alms when he was riding past on his horse. He dismounted and in a minute 'Couched' his eye and brought back his sight without demanding 'Any Satisfaction'.

The greatest of all quacks, however, was born in Norwich on 16th August, 1703, one John Taylor, later to be known as Chevalier Taylor, a title which he claimed was bestowed upon him by a foreign royal personage in addition to a long string of Doctorates of Medicine 'Honoris Causa'. He does not appear to have held any British medical qualification although he used to refer to his stay in Cambridge.

He was, in fact, the son of a surgeon in Norwich and his mother was an apothecary. He became apprenticed to an apothecary in London in 1722 and studied under Cheselden.

He published his first book at the age of twenty-three entitled *An account of the mechanism of the Eye* and this brought him to the attention of Desaguliere who advised him to become an oculist and this he did with a vengeance. However, he found it more advantageous to practise abroad since the orthodox practitioners were not at all sympathetic towards him in this country. A short period of practise in his native Norwich convinced him of the wisdom of leaving the country at intervals.

The tragedy was that he was an able man. Dr Samuel Johnson described him as the most ignorant man he had ever met, but it has been suggested that Taylor may have had the better of an argument with the worthy doctor and so became an object of his wrath. He was manually dexterous and had a very good working knowledge of the anatomy of the eye. He knew, for example, that the optic nerve pathways decussated at the chiasma and that the image of an object on the retina was inverted and that it was the brain which adjusted it again. He was the first to produce an illustration of conical cornea and invented a couching needle. He had some ideas on the subject of sympathetic ophthalmia as he did not recommend cataract extraction in one eye when the other one saw reasonably well in view of the danger of blindness in both eyes after operation. Coats, however, reports that greed overcame him and he changed his mind in later years, presumably so that he could do more operating and thus increase his income. He understood hypermetropia and myopia and also had some ideas about accommodation, but thought that the lens moved and that the extra-ocular muscles altered the length of the eyeball. He decided that the seeing layer of the eye was the choroid and, although he was quite wrong, he produced good arguments in favour of his opinion.

He knew that cataract was an opacity of the lens and not an inflammatory membrane, but his ideas on the aetiology were unusual. He described as possible causes, violent grief, or inefficient treatment of ophthalmia whereby 'the discharges are not allowed forward by kindly discutients'.

He devised a new operation of couching in which he made a bed in the vitreous below for part of the lens which he was about to displace. He divided the capsule and extruded the nucleus into this bed, the principle being that the vitreous would come forward and press against the anterior capsule taking up the shape of a lens and so avoid the necessity for a strong convex lens.

Taylor hinted that he had influenced Daviel to become an ophthalmologist and even that he extracted lenses befor him, but they never met until Daviel had been doing the operation for some six years. It is uncertain whether Taylor actually did do extractions, but he laid claims to having done so for the sake of his reputation.

His treatment of squint bordered on the scandalous. He did, however, have some idea about occlusion of the better eye, but he had very strange ideas about an operation for its cure. He used to raise a fold of conjunctiva by means of a needle and then cut through the fold with scissors. His reason for doing this was to divide a nerve filament which was supplying the contracted muscle which was causing the squint. He then covered the other eye and the squinting eye became straight. He was inclined to leave the town before the bandage had been removed. He did, however, suggest that operating on the superior oblique muscle or the medial rectus muscle might cure the squint.

His treatment of corneal opacities was either to scrape the cornea with a knife and blow in powder or to abrade the cornea with a brush made of barley bristles. There is an account given by Coats of an operation which he performed on a French priest who suffered from corneal opacities as well as cataract. He passed a gold instrument shaped at its ends like a file into the lower conjunctival sac and then bandaged the eye with the remark, 'You will see tomorrow'.

For amaurosis he pricked the extra-ocular muscles with a blunt needle to stimulate the inactive nerves by their contraction. He also massaged the eyeball with a small instrument whose surface was a little rough by which the nerves destined for the motion of the pupil were almost instantly recovered, as he thought that it was on the natural movement of the pupil that the sight depended.

His arrival at various towns was foretold by numerous pamphlets and bills rather in the manner of a circus and his entourage was correspondingly impressive. He had two coaches and six horses. His detractors declared, probably unjustly, that five of the latter were blind following their master's ministrations. He had upward of ten servants and a host of gold-plated instruments on display and it was even said, again probably unjustly, that he had eyes painted all over his carriages.

An eye-witness account of a declamation in Northampton on 7th January, 1747, is given by John Palmer, a layman who went along to hear him as he was bored with reading to pass the time during very inclement weather. He describes how he delivered his declamation from a black scaffold with a table in front of it covered with a piece of old tapestry and supporting four candles. Having distributed a hatful of incomprehensible syllabuses, he struck a suitable attitude and delivered himself of a dissertation which lasted for two hours. At the conclusion he came down and walked amongst the audience, asking them if it were not charming fine and whether they had ever heard anything like it. John Palmer admitted that he never had!

His description of glaucoma is unununderstandable. 'By glaucoma, I understand a disease'd alteration of the crystalline, where the crystalline maintains one exact equal continuity thro' all its parts, with a diseas'd alteration of its capsula attended with degrees of a very equal opacity and colour, very great increase of diameter, preternatural change of its consistence, gravity and situation; and in its last state with an elevation, dilatation and immobility of the pupil and gutta serena.'

He claimed acquaintance with royalty and the Pope. He was, in fact, appointed oculist to King George II in 1736, but some of his other claims are very extravagant.

He had the distinction of being painted by Hogarth, but unfortunately for his pride, the painting was satirical and was entitled 'The Undertaker's arms, or a Consultation of Physicians'. It depicts fifteen quacks and the three figures at the top are the Chevalier Taylor, Crazy Sally Mapp, the bone-setter, whose strength of arm was said to be exceeded only by that of her language and Spot Ward, so-called on account of a blemish on the left side of his face, who invented an antimony pill.

Coats summarises Chevalier Taylor's character thus: 'A striking and picturesque figure; of good person and address with something not unattractive in his manner; at any rate wholly unembarrassed by any diffidence in dealings with the great. An unparalleled liar, pre-eminent among Charlatans in the art of advertisement: with a natural aptitude for the grand style: rapacious in acquiring, profuse, but not generous in expending. His literary gifts were not despicable: seems to have possessed a sense of humour, and he could give and take in an encounter of wits, his public oratory must surely have been something less lugubrious than the account of his appearance at Northampton would indicate. His showy qualities imposed on many intelligent contemporaries, but by the more discerning he seems to have been regarded as an amusing rascal. In professional matters his knowledge was good: was a shrewd observer and not without original ideas; but his actual practice was deeply tainted with the dishonest arts of the quacks. Many elements go to the formation of the complete Charlatan-bombast, effrontery, dishonesty, ignorance. All these qualities Taylor showed in perfection except ignorance, and this is his chief condemnation.'

These then were the unorthodox ophthalmologists of the day. They strutted across the pages of history with all their ridiculous pomp and ignorance. There were, of course, orthodox practitioners with some knowledge of Ophthalmology, but it was a small subject in those days and specialisation was still frowned upon by many doctors. Every medical practitioner was still expected to be able to deal with any situation and, in a way, the quacks had the right idea. On the Continent, however, Beer of Vienna was instructing would-be ophthalmologists from all over the world and Daviel had introduced the operation of cataract extraction in 1756 which is still the basis of modern cataract operations. A more scientific approach to Ophthalmology was dawning and the quacks were about to become redundant and simply a rather discreditable memory.

In other fields, the Hunter Brothers from Lanarkshire, were working in London and John Hunter made his heroic experiment of infecting himself with syphilis and, although the conclusions he drew were faulty, he laid the foundations of the treatment of venereal diseases. Edward Jenner introduced vaccination against smallpox following his brilliant observations and deductions in his native Gloucestershire on milkmaids who developed cowpox sores, but not smallpox.

Both venereal diseases and smallpox in the eighteenth century were prolific causes of blindness and so the years were not altogether barren.

CHAPTER 2

The Nineteenth Century Begins

'James Mackenzie, Merchant, and Isabella Dick,
a lawful son William born 29th March, 1791.
Witnesses: Robert Gemmell and Francis Robertson.'

THUS, was the safe arrival of William Mackenzie recorded in the parochial registers of Glasgow parish. Although it would hardly cause a great stir amongst the worthy citizens of Glasgow, it did, unknowingly, mark the beginnings of the scientific era of Ophthalmology in Glasgow. The quacks had had their day and orthodox medicine was about to take its rightful place.

William Mackenzie was born in a new house in Queen Street. Until 1777, this street had been a dirty muddy lane called 'The Cow Loan' opening off Argyle Street, along which the city herdsmen drove the cattle from the Glasgow Cross area northwards to the green pastures of Cowcaddens. The ground was bought by John Neilson and laid out in lots for purchase. The houses were fine detached villas with front doors which, in many cases, opened on to a platform from which two flights of steps, one at each end, reached the street. They had narrow gardens behind and were bought or rented by the better-off citizens. Exactly which belonged to the Mackenzies is not certain, but there is some evidence that it was near the south-west corner of Queen Street close to Argyle Street. Queen Street was a very different place in 1791 from the busy commercial street of today and it contained many fine houses.

Very little is known about James and Isabella Mackenzie. Perhaps they believed in keeping themselves to themselves, just as their son William did in later years. As a family, they do not seem to have discussed their affairs very much. It is known that James Mackenzie was a muslin manufacturer and, at a time when the days of the Tobacco Lords were over and Glasgow had become a cotton town, this must have been a profitable line of business. A James Mackenzie was in business in 53 Virginia Street at this time, and the name was kept for several years after the death of William Mackenzie's father. This, however, is still not unusual in the business world.

The name of James Mackenzie also appears in the muster-roll of the old night watch of 1791. This was the forerunner of the Police Force. The Lord Provost and magistrates at that time found it necessary to establish a night guard and patrol composed of the citizens and required all male householders, citizens and inhabitants under 60 and above 18 years of age in rotation to the number of thirty-six to repair to the Laigh Kirk (Tron) Session House at 10.00 p.m., and to continue to guard and patrol till next morning. Masters of ships or workhouses and citizens whose yearly rent was 40/- or above were included, but ministers, University teachers, schoolmasters and members of the Faculty of Physicians and Surgeons and of the Faculty of Writers were exempt.

Each man was forbidden to spend more than 4d on liquor under penalty of 2/6d fine. They were to look up Buchanan Street and Spoutmouth and to report on the state of the lamps which were reputedly usually out.

On 17th December, 1786, the parochial register of Glasgow Parish tells us he married Isabella Dick, lawful daughter of the deceased William Dick, Hammerman there. Whether James Mackenzie came to seek his fortune in Glasgow from the Highlands is not known, but Isabella Dick seems to have belonged to a family of engineers in Glasgow who had been there for several generations. The Roll of Glasgow Burgesses contains the name of William Dick, Hammerman, who was admitted Burgess and Guild Brother on 24th August, 1773, as eldest lawful son to deceased William Dick, Hammerman, Burgess and Guild Brother. This may well have been her father. Again, William Dick (Senior) was similarly admitted on 5th September, 1737, and his father, David Dick, was admitted Burgess on 17th February, 1704, whilst serving his apprenticeship with James Smith, Hammerman. It seems likely, therefore, that there were three generations of Dicks before Isabella resident in Glasgow.

William was the second child of the marriage, a daughter, Margaret, was born on 22nd July, 1778, and there were no other children so far as can be ascertained. Certainly William was described as an only son when he matriculated at Glasgow University. What happened to his mother is not very clear, but it seems likely that she died when William was a boy as he makes no reference to her in his Diaries and there is no reference to her in her husband's obituary notice in the *Glasgow Herald*.

In due time, William was sent to the Glasgow Grammar School. There had been a Grammar School in Glasgow since mediaeval times. Like everything else at that time, it began near the Cathedral and Glasgow Cross, but in 1787 a new building was opened on the north side of George Street where the main door of Strathclyde University still stands. In 1787, this catered for some five hundred boys. The walk from Queen Street to the Grammar School in those days would be a very interesting one. It is unlikely, however, that young William Mackenzie would appreciate the architectural gems on the way. There was an interesting house at the southeast corner of Queen Street which had its front door opening on to Argyle Street. This had the previously mentioned platform with two flights of steps, but there was some defect in the stone and it soon turned black. It belonged to Mr John McCall, a Virginia merchant. On the west side, a little further north, there stood the fine mansion of Mr Kirkman Finlay

B

who became M.P. for the Glasgow Burghs and further north, opposite the west end of Ingram Street, stood one of the most imposing of the houses, the Lainshaw or Cunninghame mansion. This was reputed to have cost £10,000, a small fortune in those days. It became, successively the Royal Bank of Scotland, the Royal Exchange and the Stirling Library. When it became the Royal Exchange, a massive portico with large pillars was built in front of the old building and it is hard to visualise the frontage as it was. It is, in fact, still there and has been honoured with a fine equestrian statue of the Duke of Wellington erected in front of it.

A little farther north, he would come to the new George Square. This was laid down in 1782 and gradually assumed the aspect of a very fine residential square. Only the north side retains its pristine glory. At the west end of the Square was the gateway to the very fine Crawford mansion. This stood in a small estate which has become the Queen Street Station, but in those days it had an extensive rookery and, after the house had been purchased by James Ewing, the latter became known as 'Craw Ewing'.

On his way to the Grammar School, William, like all boys, would probably take the shortest route across the centre of George Square. This would be to the detriment of his boots, since the Square in those days was a muddy unkempt piece of ground, far removed from the present-day municipal centre. It gradually became enclosed and became an elegant pleasure ground, but this belonged to the future.

The City was, in fact, moving westward as it has done for many years since. The grand mansions, such as the Dreghorn mansion in Clyde Street, the Shawfield mansion at the corner of Glassford Street (where Prince Charles Edward Stuart stayed during the 1745 Rebellion) and the Virginia mansion in Virginia Street were becoming superseded by the new order farther west, and the Mackenzie family were part of the pattern.

William Mackenzie was a good scholar and his pious father decided that he was to become a minister of the Church of Scotland. Accordingly, he left school and went to Glasgow University at the early age, even for those days, of twelve, to study Arts. His matriculation is recorded in 1803 and he is described as the only son of James Mackenzie. He was an accomplished classical scholar as is evident from some of his later writings.

Unfortunately, James Mackenzie died on 9th May, 1805, shortly after William's fourteenth birthday. This must have been a great grief to his two children, but Margaret Mackenzie would, by now, be eighteen and probably looked after the housekeeping. It is not possible to determine how long they stayed in the Queen Street house, but in later years, even before he came back to Glasgow in 1819, he seems to have owned a house at 5 North Albion Street which must have been a little south of the *Citizen* Office of today. It is unlikely that the Mackenzies were left badly off. Admittedly William's education at the Grammar School was not expensive., In 1815, it is reported that the Rector received 15/- and the Masters 10/6d for each pupil and the fees were even less in Mackenzie's time. Each boy took a four-year course and stayed with the same Master all the time. When the class reached its fourth year, the Master became the Principal. The fees were only 6/- per quarter, plus a 'Trifle to the Janitor'. The fees at the University were, of course, much higher and two to three guineas per class was usual. There would be no ready means of subsidising them. Still, he never seems to have wanted for anything.

When William was still a toddler, Britain went to war with France and so his education was overshadowed by the Napoleonic Wars and he did not qualify in Medicine until the year of Waterloo which finally brought the war to an end. He was a student when the Nelson Monument was erected on Glasgow Green in 1806 and was probably studying Divinity when his fellow Glaswegian, Sir John Moore, was killed at Corunna in 1809.

It seemed to be quite common for promising young men to be destined for the Church and then to change their minds. The great William Hunter was sent to Glasgow University to study Divinity and then gave it up to study Medicine in Edinburgh. William Mackenzie completed his Arts course, but does not seem to have graduated. He studied Divinity, but appears to have had doubts about his suitability to be a clergyman. It is said that the story of the Creation worried him and he sought a more scientific explanation. In this respect, he resembled Charles Darwin who went farther and promulgated his 'Origin of Species' after painstaking thought and research. There is no record of William Mackenzie's thoughts on Darwin's theory, but one can surmise that he would be thrilled when he read about it. Interestingly enough, Charles Darwin was also earmarked for the Church, but as one would expect, he finished up severely criticised by the clergy for daring to doubt the Old Testament story. What the Church lost from these three scientists one will never know, but Medicine was very much the better off. Mackenzie pondered many another problem in his time and Ophthalmology was much the better of it.

Having made his decision, he began to study Medicine in 1810 at Glasgow University. He did not qualify in the more usual way by serving an apprenticeship with a medical practitioner, but chose to study at the University, thus pursuing a more academic line of study. Usually, the medical students presented themselves for examination in the Faculty of Physicians and Surgeons of Glasgow after an apprenticeship of three years. The regulations were that the candidate had to prove that he had attended a course of lectures at the University, one of the Royal Colleges or the Glasgow Faculty. This consisted of lectures in Anatomy, Surgery, Materia Medica, Chemistry and Midwifery. If no apprenticeship had been done, the candidate had to show that he had attended the practice of a public hospital for one year and also of a surgeon's or apothecary's shop for six months. As Mackenzie had not served an apprenticeship, he became a resident clerk with Dr Richard Miller at the Glasgow Royal Infirmary from 1813 to 1815.

The disadvantage of taking a University medical degree in Glasgow before 1815 was that it was almost entirely academic. There was no real systematic training and no clinical instruction. The only subjects taught were anatomy, Physiology, Pathology and Materia Medica. The term 'physician' was reserved for those who qualified with the degree of M.D. After 1815, when Chairs of Surgery and Midwifery were established, a candidate for the degree had to have attended classes for at least three years, exactly half of what is required now, including three sessions of six months each in Anatomy and Surgery, two sessions each of the Theory and Practice of Medicine, two sessions of Chemistry, Materia Medica and Pharmacy, and one session each of Botany and Midwifery.

On the face of it, the University course looks much more efficient, but it demanded no clinical experience and many M.D.'s were purely academic. Thus, the apprenticeship was still the backbone of medical education. The Faculty strongly guarded itself against the University graduates and compelled them to practise as physicians only. The physicians, on the other hand, regarded the 'surgeons' who qualified by the apprenticeship method as inferior and allied to barbers, although they did make up the general practitioners of the day.

The Faculty of Physicians and Surgeons, however, remained the only Licencing Authority in theory and jealously guarded this right even to raising an action in 1815 against four M.D.'s who were practising without a licence from the Faculty. The Faculty won its case. Mackenzie had, as it were, the best of both worlds. His chief in the Royal Infirmary, Dr Richard Miller, was a distinguished physician who became the first Professor of Materia Medica and Mackenzie was with him for two years. During this time, he met two of his lifelong friends, Harry Rainy, son of the minister of Creich, Sutherland, and James Armour, son of a tailor in Fenwick. Mackenzie was, of course, still in the Royal Infirmary during the Napoleonic Wars and in 1814 he received a letter from an old student friend, Dr Thomas Brisbane, describing the Battle of Toulouse in which he took part as a surgeon. This was the battle which need not have taken place as Napoleon had abdicated four days previously. News travelled slowly in 1814. Dr Brisbane was apprehensive about his future and wrote that he felt sure that the country would be over-run by half-starved army and navy surgeons since the war was over, but he came home safely and became a general practitioner in Largs. He does not seem to have been one of Mackenzie's closer friends. He does not seem to have been a direct descendent of the famous Sir Thomas Macdougall Brisbane who was Governor of New South Wales and gave his name to the city, but he was almost certainly a relative. His father was minister of Dunlop, Ayrshire.

Harry Rainy was in London in 1814 and was attending the Eye Infirmary in Charterhouse Square which was to become the Moorfields Eye Hospital, and also the Lock Hospital. He was very complimentary about the work at the Eye Infirmary, but not about the students he met. 'Several students are puppies, but several of them are extremely clever', he wrote. The surgeons at that time were Doctors Farre, Travers and Lawrence and Rainy considered Dr Farre the best, although he thought his manner disagreeable at first. Travers, he discovered, extracted all his cataracts and did not couch them. There were about twelve students and the fee was five guineas. The students, he felt, were treated with more respect than in Scotland.

On the subject of the Lock Hospital, Rainy was far from complimentary. It was, he wrote, dirty and ill-arranged and only one of the chiefs, Dr McGregor, attended regularly. He described him, however, as a good-natured pleasant good-for-nothing. One of the other doctors, Dr Pearson, he thought more intelligent, but left much of the work to his house-surgeon whom Rainy described as a self-sufficient, ignorant coxcomb. The third chief, Dr Blair, apparently harldy ever attended at all and was always in a hurry when he did so.

Rainy also attended St Bartholomew's Hospital where he was surprised to find only four hundred patients. He wrote about seeing Blücher, Alexander and Wellington frequently and the last eclipsed all the others. He also wrote that there was to be a ridiculous exhibition in the parks presumably to entertain the Prince Regent. He was not too narrow-minded to disapprove of theatre-going and we find him criticising the acting in London. He went to opera on one occasion, but described it as 'Extravagant Nonsense'. It bored him and he felt that one guinea for a good seat and 10/6d for the pit was far too much. He also made reference in his letter to 'Wee Scuddy' whom he described as 'Dashing away in grand style'. 'His relations, or at least his wife's relations, move in the first circles'. The implication that he was ambitious, however, seems to have not been too wide of the mark, for this was almost certainly Sir Charles Scudamore who graduated M.D. Glasgow in 1814, and became a general practitioner in Highgate and later a physician in London. He was appointed physician to Prince Leopold of Saxe Gotha and later to the Duke of Northumberland when Lord Lieutenant of Ireland.

Mackenzie became interested in the anatomy and physiology of the eye as a student, but for several years was undecided whether to specialise in it. Perhaps Harry Rainy's letter helped him to decide. At any rate, he sent him a list of books on Ophthalmology and it looks as if Mackenzie had at least discussed the matter with his friend.

In September 1814, Rainy went over to France and attended the practice of Dupuytren, Orfilla and Roux. He was still there when the news of Napoleon's escape from Elba came through. Brisbane had written to Mackenzie describing the joy of the French people when Napoleon abdicated and the Bourbons were reinstated in 1814. Rainy, however, implied that the joy was the same when he came back to France. Truly the mob is fickle! Rainy decided to leave Paris at once in the circumstances and made for Belgium by way of Metz. He is reputed to have crossed the field of Waterloo, a few weeks before the famous Battle in June 1815. Thus, he came back to Glasgow where he renewed his acquaintance with Mackenzie and Armour who were about to set out on their chosen careers. Dupuytren had offered his protection if he stayed in Paris, but Rainy, not surprisingly, played for safety and made for home.

Whilst in the Royal Infirmary, Mackenzie became secretary of the Medical Society, but during his long life he took very little part in committee work or, for that matter, in public life of any kind.

In November 1814, he received a note from Dr Robert Graham asking him to bleed 'Pattison'. Dr Graham graduated M.D. in 1808 and became a physician at the Royal Infirmary in 1812. He was later appointed Professor of Botany in Glasgow University, but in 1814 he was anxious about a gentleman called Pattison and wished Mackenzie to bleed him from the jugular vein since he was still suffering from severe headaches in spite of purgation. If the patient referred to was Granville Pattison, it is not surprising that he was suffering from headaches since he attracted trouble as a jam pot does wasps. He was a very able man, a teacher of Anatomy and Surgery and, like all anatomists in those days, engaged in obtaining cadavers for dissection illegally by 'Resurrection'. Shortly before this date on 6th June, he had stood trial in Glasgow for this offence. The young men employed by him had apparently gone to the Ramshorn Churchyard and had dug up the body of the wife of a much respected tradesman called McAllister, in error. The young men were discovered in the act and chased to Pattison's dissecting rooms where the body was hastily concealed under the floor. The police made a careful search and, at first, found nothing. On closer inspection, the trap-door was found and the body recognised by the appearance of the teeth. At the time, however, the prosecution was unable to establish beyond reasonable doubt that the body was, in fact, that of Mrs McAllister and Pattison was acquitted due to lack of evidence. It is said that somehow the anatomists interchanged the parts of two separate cadavers. Five months later, however, Granville Pattison seems to have had headaches. Perhaps another lawsuit was pending. His destiny was later interwoven with that of Mackenzie and the latter was able to start his career as a lecturer in Glasgow when Pattison left it for good.

William Mackenzie's great day came on 7th August, 1815, when he became a Licentiate of the Faculty of Physicians and Surgeons of Glasgow and, in the words of the official document which he signed, swore to God that he would exercise the several parts of his profession as pharmacian to the best of his knowledge and abilities and that he would not knowingly or intentionally do anything or administer anything to any person to their hurt or prejudice for any consideration or from any motive whatever. The declaration finished with the words 'So help me God'. The licence cost fifteen guineas and the membership one hundred guineas up to 1815 when it went up to one hundred and fifty guineas. This seemed to Mackenzie too

I Solemnly Swear by God that I will ex:
ercise the several parts of my profession as
Veterinarian to the best of my knowledge & ability
and that I will not knowingly or intentionally
do any thing or administer any thing to
any Person to their hurt or prejudice
for any consideration or from any motive
whatever So help me God.

Sept 7th 1812   James Jackson

                       John Mure

                       William Robertson

Dec 5th }———————— James Forsyth
1825   }

March 6th 1826 ———————— Thomas Cameron

                       John Robertson
May 8th 1826   John Kirkpatrick
May 19th 1826   David Hutton
May 26   D M Galpine
May 26th 1826 Greenock William Gibson
May 26th 1826 Aberdeen Andrew Hutton
June 1826   John Bulloch
5 June 1826   David Millar
John Phillips Dumblane Perthshire

✓ Thomas McCreath ... lie Bucanshire 3 July 1815

✓ John Tait Paisley Renfrewshire 3 July 1815

✓ John Caldwell Glasgow — 17 July 1815

✓ Donald MacLachlan Argyleshire 17 July 1815

✓ Alexander Poole Armagh Augt 7th 1815

✓ William Mac Kenzie, Glasgow, 7th August, 1815.

✓ Thomas Lightbody Glasgow 21 August 1815

✓ John Hutchison Glasgow 21st August 1815

✓ James Cameron Glasgow 21st August 1815

✓ John Mathieson Glasgow 2nd October 1815

✓ John McLaws Campsie Stirlingshire 2 Octobr 1815

✓ John King Irvine 11 Octobr 1815

✓ John Mackison Kilsyth 7 Novr 1815

✓ John McFarlane Old Kilpatrick 7th Novr 1815

✓ Michael Barker Young Mong thorn 7 Novemober 1815

✓ Duncan MacCalman Argyleshire 7th Novr 1815

✓ Robert Gray Glasgow 16 Decr 1815

✓ Duncan McKenzie Glasgow 18 Decr 1815

✓ John McFarlane Glasgow 5th Feby 1816

✓ James Maxwell Glasgow Feby 27th 1816

✓ James Singer Glasgow March 4 1816

✓ Samuel Mitchell Glasgow March 4 1816

✓ Andrew McLeod Glasgow April 1 1816

✓ William Scott Kilmarnock Ayre 1 1816

expensive since the examination for both was the same and only prestige was involved.

Thus began William Mackenzie's medical career which brought about the founding of an Eye Infirmary, the writing of the first comprehensive textbook of Ophthalmology in the English language, several other books and countless articles, a royal appointment and an international reputation.

George Square, Glasgow, *circa* 1830. Mackenzie lived in the block of houses to the left of the tall statue. Copied by the Author from *George Square* published about 1889.

CHAPTER 3

The Grand Tour: London and Paris

IT WAS fashionable at the beginning of the nineteenth century for young men of substance to do a grand tour of the Continent before settling down. The young medicals of the age did something of the same, if they could afford it, but on a much more modest scale and with a more cultural slant. They no doubt enjoyed themselves as well, but in some respects, the Continent was ahead of Great Britain and this was particularly so in Ophthalmology.

When Mackenzie qualified in 1815, there was one eye specialist in Glasgow, George Cunningham Monteath. He was a little older than Mackenzie having been born in 1788, but they had known each other as students. George Monteath had had to cut his tour of the other medical schools short due to the French Wars, but he did attend the Eye Infirmary in Charterhouse Square in London. Harry Rainy, as we have seen already, did a tour of France which was interrupted by the resumption of the War in 1815 and Mackenzie, whose finances always seem to have been adequate, determined on an extensive tour of the Continent, but he went to London first early in 1816. He took lodgings in Smithfield and attended St Bartholomew's Hospital, like Rainy before him. There he attended the practice of the famous John Abernethy and kept a record of the surgical patients he saw which is still extant.

Whilst he was in London, James Armour wrote rather plaintively from Glasgow asking about Mackenzie's plans for the future. 'Will you give up your plans for lecturing in Glasgow', he wrote. 'Do you mean to go on with the plans with you and I working together, or will they be laid aside? You know the state of my finances and my deficiencies in anatomical knowledge, and I must now think very seriously how I must act, because I am under the disagreeable necessity of borrowing money to pay the Faculty.'

Armour had, in fact, just passed his examination for the Licence with flying colours. He wrote, 'I passed the examination which was, with me, a mere form. One who is examined before me is examined for forty minutes, the one after me for an hour and a quarter. I passed in five minutes. Mr Brown told me that they meant to put a few questions, because they knew perfectly well what I knew. It was as well he did – otherwise, he might have discovered my extreme ignorance. I have made up my medicine, and I am to write an essay on the Foetal Circulation – a foolish subject, you will perhaps say. On the 4th of May, upon paying my money, I suppose I will be admitted.'

The young doctors in those days were under the necessity of supplementing their income by one means or another, whilst building up their practices and lecturing was one way of doing it. Extramural schools were springing up all over the place and in 1815, it was estimated that there were eight hundred students studying Anatomy and Surgery in Glasgow of whom only two hundred and fifty were studying under Professor Jeffrey at the University. James Armour was keen to start something of the kind, but his finances would not allow it and Mackenzie always seems to have had enough. When the latter departed for London, Armour felt his chances were not so rosy. How much Mackenzie regarded lecturing in Anatomy and Surgery as a stepping-stone towards a career as an ophthalmologist and how much as an end in itself, it is impossible to say, but he seemed to keep an open mind for quite a long time. What he replied to Armour is, of course, unknown, but he was probably already planning his extensive Continental tour and would be unlikely to feel that he wanted to be tied down at this early stage.

He attended the Eye Infirmary in Charterhouse Square and probably the Lock Hospital also, just as Rainy had done. He wrote to Rainy at one point asking about the chances of lecturing in Glasgow, all the same, and the latter replied giving details of the cost of rooms in the Deanhead Brae. It looks then as if he had not yet finally decided to go to the Continent and he may have had James Armour in mind as a partner.

However, he seems to have made up his mind in the spring of 1816, for Rainy sent him a letter of introduction to his old chief in Paris, M. Roux at the Charité. He sent two more letters, one to a Greek doctor whom they called Michel, his surname apparently being unpronounceable, and another one to an old friend from his student days in Edinburgh, James Arnott. The latter was destined to become a close friend of Mackenzie's too and, at this time, he was studying in Paris at the Jardin des Plantes. Rainy said that he had the reputation of possessing a considerable share of good sense and prudence and an inflexible integrity which Mackenzie would find a rather rare feature in the characters he would meet in Paris. He also wrote that Arnott had seen much of the Continent and would be able to help Mackenzie in arranging his plans of study and, what is more, in doing this as economically as possible.

So it was that Mackenzie set off from London on the morning of Monday, 6th May, 1816, and arrived in Brighton that evening. At half-past nine the following morning he went on board the Packet for Dieppe, hoping to arrive that evening, but the wind died down in the late afternoon just as they came in sight of France. They had been doing nine knots, but now Mackenzie decided there was no hope of reaching Dieppe that night and he very sensibly went to bed. He went on Deck at 5.00 a.m., to find that the Packet was already in Harbour and to his surprise, saw a crucifix on the pier. This was apparently the first time that he had seen one erected for what he called 'The excitement of adoration'. Glasgow must have been very Presbyterian in those days!

Three hours later he boarded the cabriolet of the diligence for Rouen and thus began his Continental tour which was to last about two years. It was to take him through France, Switzerland, Italy, Austria-Hungary and Germany and took him to many well-known centres of medical study which was to have a profound influence on his life.

He did most of his travelling by horse-drawn and occasionally mule-drawn transport of various kinds, but he did part of it by river-boat and even by sea at one point. He met many interesting people, including some of the British Army who were still in occupation of France, but perhaps the high light was his meeting in Pavia with the famous Antonio Scarpa, who was by this time an elderly man.

His health remained good, but he had a few attacks of travel-sickness which is not surprising, and had to break his journey at one point on account of distressing colic. The lodgings which he occupied were often very uncomfortable and he did not always succeed in securing a bed, spending the night on straw on the floor, and on one occasion he left his room and spent the night in the coach because he had been attacked by fleas. Here, he was soon joined by a fellow-traveller for the same reason.

He always seemed to have enough money for his needs and was able to pay for his transport. At the same time as he was on his way home, three young medical graduates from Utrecht, Tilanus, Broers and de Fremery set out on a tour of France and Germany. They went by coach as far as Strasbourg, but toured Germany on foot. Whether this was by choice or from necessity, it is impossible to say. Their undergraduate medical training had been strangely similar to that of Mackenzie and they visited some of the same clinics as did Mackenzie. Their tour was, however, not as extensive and, strangely enough, did not include Vienna which was, at that time, at the height of its fame.

Mackenzie succeeded in learning French, Italian and German during his tour, but he was already proficient in the Classics and knew some French before he set out. After nine days in France, however, he resolved to take lessons as he found that he could neither read French with the proper pronunciations, nor speak it correctly, nor understand when he was spoken to.

He was a poor correspondent, it seems, since his friends were frequently moved to scold him for not answering their letters. This was particularly so in the case of James Armour, who seemed to have an inferiority complex and, on occasions, accused Mackenzie of becoming rather high and mighty. Mackenzie, however, seems to have been a modest man and Armour was probably imagining things. Harry Rainy was a frequent correspondent and seemed to be regarded as an adviser by the others. Perhaps the most prolific letter writer was the Rev. Adam Boyd, whom Mackenzie had met in the Faculty of Divinity and who, at this time, was acting as tutor to a young man. Unfortunately, he had the habit of writing a letter, then turning it through a right angle and writing across the previous paragraphs. This makes it impossible to read them now. Another friend who wrote on occasions was the light-hearted James Sym, one of four brothers. One of the latter, George Oswald Sym, who was also a Divinity student died young, before being ordained and Mackenzie received a letter during this Continental tour telling him of his first haemoptysis which heralded the onset of the tuberculosis which killed him.

On 9th May, 1816, Mackenzie arrived in Paris early in the morning and recalled, rather sadly, in his Diary that his father for whom he seems to have had a great affection, had died exactly eleven years previously to the day.

He settled in the Hotel des Etrangers and set out to find 'Michel' to whom he had a letter of introduction from Rainy. It transpired that his surname was Kontzofsky and that the French had great difficulty in pronouncing it, although the British found it a little easier. It took Mackenzie a whole day to find him since he had been changing his lodgings frequently, which suggests that he had been failing to pay his rent.

After attending some lectures in the Jardin des Plantes on Natural History, Mackenzie found his way to the Hotel Dieu and attended the practice of the great Dupuytren. The Hotel Dieu at this time held some fifteen hundred patients and the description of some of the cases and of the death-rate was truly appalling, although no different from that which would be found at any other hospital in 1816. Mackenzie, however, was critical of his method of treating fractures which he describes as more 'Severe' than the English one. A patient with one thigh and the other leg fractured died of 'Irritative Fever' for example. The suggestion seems to be that the bandages were too tight and the limb became gangerous. Cutting for the stone was sometimes fatal in Dupuytren's hands, as it was with many surgeons of those days, but Mackenzie found much to admire in Dupuytren's methods of treatment. The three young Dutchmen described him as being intensely ambitious. He had gained promotion in the Hotel Dieu over the head of Roux and there was something of a feud between the two men. Roux unfortunately at one point reported to his students that a young woman patient of a celebrated and eloquent surgeon had died following the extirpation of a tumour under the mastoid muscle. Dupuytren recognised the reference to himself and during one of his lectures refuted the calumny in strong terms. 'A man who wishes to distinguish himself as an author without knowing how to write, who gives gratis a course of lectures which nobody wishes to attend, and who has published a Journey to England which nobody can be found to read, has lately taken the liberty to report the death of a young lady whom I have now the pleasure to present to you recovered after the extirpation of a tumour from the mastoid muscle.' The book to which Dupuytren referred was a description of Roux's visit to London in 1814. Like Rainy in the opposite direction, he had taken advantage of the temporary cessation of hostilities in Europe to come to England to visit the London hospitals. He was very struck by the large number of hospitals which were functioning in buildings specially built for the purpose, but he was a little critical of the diversity of authority over each hospital. In Paris in 1814, all hospitals were under a central authority, which could be regarded as something of an integrated Health Service. Mackenzie, who had an introduction to Roux from Rainy must have watched this difference of opinion between the two great men with interest.

Dupuytren was, in fact, a little less than fair about Roux's book. Although it is always a little risky to write about the ways in which other people organise their affairs, the book gave praise as well as criticism and probably did something to heal the rift which must have existed between France and Britain in those days.

Another lecturer whom Mackenzie attended was Alibert in the Hôpital St Louis. He went there with James Arnott whom he had contacted thanks to Rainy's introduction. They were very amused by Alibert's whole arrangements. In the first place, he conducted his demonstrations of cases of diseases of the skin under the trees in the hospital grounds. He was surrounded by old and young of both sexes, including the patients, and also the students. The whole motley crowd of academics were treated to extravagant gesticulations from Alibert and Mackenzie remarked that he might have been taken for a mountebank or a Methodist! But there was no doubting his earnest endeavours to communicate information. In another lecture the following week, Alibert described a female patient with depraved appetite who swallowed an immense quantity of needles and pins and a man who ate live rabbits!

In a fit of enthusiasm, he went to the Hôpital des Vénérièns at 5.30 a.m., and attended the visit of M. Cullerier! The latter was a very quick worker and visited two hundred and fifty patients and prescribed for them in an hour and a quarter. The standard treatment was, of course, mercury, but Cullerier had tried muriate of gold for syphillis, without success.

A visit to the Institution for the Deaf and Dumb was of great interest to Mackenzie. The demonstration was a public one given by the Abbé Sicard who gave illustrations of how these unfortunate people were being educated, particularly a young man of twenty-five who had progressed very far in the art of writing and also in philosophical grammar and metaphysics.

All his time, however, was not spent with medical men in hospitals. He made friends with a Lieutenant Hodgkin who took him out to St Denis to meet an old friend from Glasgow, Mr Alexander Angus who, along with other military surgeons, was preparing to leave for Cambrai. Mackenzie was tickled at the grumbles of these 'Veterans' of one year's standing that their services were no longer required, the war having stopped too soon for their liking. Alexander Angus was the son of a teacher at an academy in Ingram Street, Glasgow, and was admitted to the Faculty in 1819.

At a later date he went to the Champs de Mars with Lieutenant Hodgkin and another officer, a Quaker called Sams, the latter in full-dress uniform, in order to see the presentation of colours to the National Guard. He then proceeded to the Chamber of Deputies, took a hasty look at the Louvre and, in the evening, on his way to a social engagement saw Mlle Garnavin, descend by means of a parachute from a balloon. Quite an eventful day!

On 19th June, Mackenzie received a visit from Mr William Ewing of Glasgow who was visiting Paris with some friends. It is likely that Mr Ewing was an old friend of his father since there was a firm of cloth merchants carrying on business in the Trongate under the name of Patrick Ewing & Co., and one of the partners was called William. This would be something in the nature of a link with the past for the young Scot. Another meeting outside medical contacts was with the Rev. Stair McQuhae who was to become minister of St Quivox in Prestwick. He was a graduate of Glasgow University and possibly met Mackenzie in the Faculty of Divinity. Together they examined the monuments in the Museum des Monuments Français where they met. These had been pilfered from the rest of Europe and were considered very fine, but Mackenzie did not admire them very much. They were, he wrote, 'A mixture of trash and names unknown. What a different effect from the Monument of Smollet at Renton', he added with great loyalty to his native land.

Mackenzie was always interested in the people around him. At one point he records his disgust at some people he saw. These he described as 'Crowds of wretched Englishmen in the Palais Royal, admiring the miserable Café de mille Colonnes, and the smart whore who sits at the bar. Why do men come to make fools of themselves here? Some of them can't speak three words of French. Everything they buy they give triple its value for. Here is one with a diarrhoea who has forsooth been tempted to swallow some fashionable Ragout which his English bowels, more honest than himself insist upon getting rid of. Here is another who has taken into keeping a nice enough little French girl, whose chit-chat however might have been as well wasted on a post as on an animal who falls asleep even in the midst of wantonness.'

All through his travels one finds such comments on his fellow-travellers and chance acquaintances, and it is this interest in people which contributes so much to the success of a doctor in his practice. Whilst he was in Paris, Mackenzie was intrigued by the preparations in Notre Dame for the wedding of the Duc de Berri and he later witnessed the arrival of the King with the Duchesse d'Angouleme, the Duc de Berri and his bride Carolina from Fontainbleau by the Boulevards and the Place Vendôme. He was not greatly impressed by the bride's appearance and reported that she looked like a plain country girl. However, he seems to have been impressed by the cuirassiers who were guarding the procession and whom he was seeing for the first time.

The following day, 17th June, was their wedding day and Mackenzie went to see the Duke of Wellington with the foreign ambassadors pass over the Pont Neuf to the Tuilleries. In the evening, all Paris was illuminated. There was time for theatre-going too and in the following week, he went to the Academy of Music with his friends Hodgkin, Sams and Angus to see the 'Deux Rivaux' in honour of the Duc de Berri's marriage. He was not very enamoured of this and wrote that he was, in general, tired with the singing and not at all pleased with the unnatural dancing. The following Sunday he went to the Odeon with Kontsofsky and a M. Seraphine to see 'La Grande Ville' and 'La Petite Ville'. His only comment was that the first was like 'The Provoked Husband' and the second like 'Raising the Wind'. He made no remark about the fact that going to the theatre on a Sunday would not have been possible in his native Glasgow in 1816.

There is no doubt that Mackenzie had a sense of humour, for on 29th June he records in his Diary, 'It seems that Chaussier began his course of lectures on Physiology during the Consulship of Bonaparte. While the latter has been created Emperor, has repudiated his wife, married the daughter of the Emperor of Germany, been dethroned and replaced and defeated and exiled, M. Chaussier has not finished his history of the little we know of the animal economy. He left off last session in the middle of digestion.'

Shortly before this, in more sombre mood, however, he had written, 'It is dangerous for a foreigner to pronounce after a week's residence in a large City, during which he has regularly followed the practice of the Hospitals, upon the merits of the Surgery of the country. If he is inclined to blame severely what he thinks faulty, if he is inclined to look with prejudice upon what is different from the practice of his own country, he will probably wander very far from a true and just representation. If he be inclined to indiscriminate praise of what is to him novel and foreign, he may perhaps do still a greater injury to truth.' He had, in fact, been critical of some of the treatment he had seen, but very few young doctors can resist this particular temptation.

William Mackenzie left Paris at 7.00 a.m., on Monday, 8th July, 1816, in the diligence for Geneva. His visit, therefore, lasted almost exactly two months. He had seen much, both medical and otherwise. He had met many people, many of them Scottish as is only natural, and had seen the aftermath of a great conflict. He had apparently mastered the French language for he used it on occasion in other countries and he had contrived to enjoy himself too. One is impressed, however, by the amount of hospital work which he did which, after all, was the main purpose of his visit.

WILLIAM MACKENZIE

WILLIAM MACKENZIE

This portrait of William Mackenzie was presented to him by the Directors of the
Glasgow Eye Infirmary in 1859.

CHAPTER 4

The Grand Tour: Geneva, Rome and Naples

THE DILIGENCE travelled along the road from Paris to Dijon. At 10.00 a.m., it stopped at Villeneuve St Georges to allow the passengers to dine, but Mackenzie had no great appetite for cutlets and sausages at that time in the forenoon and, having sniffed the smells emanating from the kitchen which were not to his liking, proceeded on foot towards the next staging post. It was a lovely day and he watched a ploughman using a plough with two wheels behind two horses. The ploughman asked Mackenzie if they had such ploughs in England and was reassured on this point.

There was much discussion amongst the passengers and it was asserted by a French captain that, had the Duc d'Angoulême been in command at Waterloo, Wellington would have been defeated. The captain did not have a great opinion of Bonaparte as a general, but others of the company did.

At Poligny, Mackenzie sampled the Vin d'Arboise and pronounced it superior to champagne. That night they ascended Jura and Mackenzie walked a considerable way, perhaps to lighten the load or perhaps to sober himself up, for he admits that he was quite tipsy after enjoying the wine of Arboise. In the next sentence he recorded in his Diary that he had seen a pretty girl, but after all one is apt to forget that he was only twenty-five and far from home and a little wine and a pretty face would cheer him up no end.

On 12th July, he arrived in Geneva and duly visited the hospital which contained some three hundred patients although it could take in two hundred more. It was remarkable for not having an operating-room. From Geneva he was able to see Mont Blanc and La Mole and the latter, he wrote in his Diary, had nearly the shape of Ben Lomond. He was entranced by Lake Geneva and recorded that he was of the opinion that Calvin, whom he does not seem to have admired very much in spite of his Presbyterian upbringing, must have spent his time regarding the gloomy mountains of Jura, not the beautiful Lake. He did notice the large number of women with goitres in Geneva, but although he noticed that most of the Genevese women seemed to have a fulness of the neck, he did not see any monstrous cases.

Four days after his arrival, he left Geneva in a carriage for which he had bargained with a Voiturier to take him to Milan for eighty-five francs. He

C

was not the only passenger and this part of the tour was one of the most interesting of all, chiefly on account of the scenery, but also on account of his fellow-travellers who were largely military men. They left Geneva at 5.00 a.m., and soon entered the Sardinian Dominions where the examination of one's baggage could be avoided by a payment to the customs officers. The King of Sardinia had been touring his kingdom and Aix-le-Bains was gay with decorations as they arrived. Mackenzie went to see the famous Baths, but declined to taste the waters. At Chambery he wrote about busying himself, along with the others, in basting the chickens for supper and it looks as if service was not always included in bill of fare at the inns.

At Montmellian, they were joined by a captain in the Sardinian Army. He was a diminutive man, so small, in fact, that his batman had to lift him in and out of the carriage. Mackenzie got a lot of fun out of him and always referred to him as the 'Wee Sardinian'. He wore a broad yellow sash and a large cocked hat which would only accentuate his lack of inches. An amusing feature of this encounter is that Mackenzie himself was reputed to be only about five feet tall and if the 'Wee Sardinian' were smaller than this, he must have been very tiny indeed. Mackenzie was not the only one in the carriage to be amused by him. Also in the company was a remarkable German captain aged sixty-two, who had been forty-five years in the Army and was something of a humorist. His advice to the 'Wee Sardinian' was to eat two eggs with soup and wine for breakfast and a pigeon at night instead of the two pills which the doctor had ordered.

Mackenzie was put out when the 'Wee Sardinian' asked him whether a Protestant in Geneva was allowed to marry a Christian, but he had a lot of fun watching him. At one inn, he imperiously told the landlady that the the King had ordered that he should have a special room to himself, but that he was not always successful is demonstrated by Mackenzie's description of him trying to climb on to a rather high bed with the aid of a chair climbing like a cat.

At Modena, Mackenzie was vastly amused when he read one of the Sardinian laws which stated that it was not legal for hotel-keepers to give anybody meat or fatty eatables on days prohibited by the Church, save only to invalids. It happened to be a Friday and the first thing the good woman of the inn did was to prepare a meal of meat and fat eatables. 'I suppose she looked upon us in the light of patients', Mackenzie wrote in his Diary.

The road climbed gradually up to the Mont Cénis Pass and the horses were replaced by four mules which were hired for six francs. The road was a new one, built in 1800 and the old road could be seen covered in grass. Formerly the carriage had to be taken to bits and loaded on the backs of mules which cost the travellers five francs each and a good deal of time.

As they climbed, Mackenzie became entranced by the scenery. He had been looking forward to this part of the journey for a long time and he was not disappointed. As time went on, the scenery became more savage and fascinating and the 'Wee Sardinian's' entertainment value slumped.

At the frontier, the driver asked the passengers to alight and cross by means of a footpath whilst he drove the empty carriage across on the road. By this means, he was able to avoid paying a tiresome tax! Mackenzie became very interested in the wild flowers and was almost left behind at one point, being out of sight frequently whilst looking for new plants.

On 21st July, he arrived at Turin and duly visited the hospital there. He was interested to encounter one of the physicians paying his visit in full dress peroque and bag, sword, laced coat and flowered vest. In Turin he was surprised to see offices for the sale of indulgences and also for confession with the promise of an indulgence.

On 23rd July, in excessively hot weather, he went on towards Milan in another coach. In the evening, he dined at Vercelli to the accompaniment of three guitars and wrote, 'Here may be said to begin Italian luxury'. Unfortunately, when he left Vercelli and passed through Novara he did not have his passport stamped and so, when he reached the Custom Post near Ticino, he had to send his passport back with a gendarme and wait at the frontier at the cost of thirteen francs. He was kept there from 10.15 a.m., until 6.00 p.m., without anything to eat. He had not any great opinion of the Piedmontese whom he had met on the road, but this incident did nothing to improve it. He arrived in Milan on 25th July and went along at once to the Cathedral which he deemed equal, but not superior to St. Paul's.

As usual, he visited the hospital which had a false frontage and a large capacity (it was reputed to hold up to three thousand patients). The chapel too was very large and reputed to hold thirty thousand people, or so he wrote. In the afternoon he set off on what was to be one of the most memorable of his journeys, towards Pavia, for he had a great ambition to visit the celebrated Italian anatomist, Antonio Scarpa. He arrived at 7.00 p.m., and set off to look for the hospital, but was forced to ask the way from a gentleman in the street. It transpires that he was a medical man, called Corneliani and he took him under his wing and accompanied him to the hospital. He had been assistant to Scarpa for some three years and had been ten years qualified. He told Mackenzie that Scarpa had retired and was living in the country and that one of the surgeons had been a Bonapartist, as a result of which, he was a prisoner of the Austrians.

In the Anatomical Museum, he saw some wonderful wax models, one of the third, fourth, fifth and sixth cranial nerves and some of a complete body showing the veins of the body. By lifting away the front, the intestines could be seen. These had been made as early as 1801 by Supini in Florence. There was an interesting comment by Nosconi of Pavia in a pamphlet issued shortly before Mackenzie arrived, on the political effects of vaccination. He considered that the latter would certainly greatly increase the population of Italy and was likely to increase by so doing, the misery of the poor. This is the same sort of problem which still faces the world today.

Mackenzie employed some of his time with Corneliani translating into Italian Dr Graham's case of obstructed aorta, a copy of which he had brought with him. Some of his time was spent shopping for some of Scarpa's books and in the course of this, he was shown over Scarpa's picture-gallery and study. In the latter, he found some medical books in English including his old friend, Wardrop's book on Fungus Haematodes.

It must have been a disappointment to Mackenzie to find that Scarpa was living in the country, but on 7th August, Corneliani introduced him to a priest called De Antoni who persuaded him that he should go to see Scarpa along with Corneliani. So the next day they set out for Bosnano. They slept the night on the way and arrived at Scarpa's country house at the unearthly hour of 6.00 a.m. They were tactful enough to wait until the old gentleman had risen before Corneliani sent up his name and mentioned that he had a young surgeon from Scotland with him. It transpired that he knew that such a one was in the district as Cajioli had sent him a note from Pavia saying that a Scot had been inquiring about the price of Scarpa's books.

When they entered, Scarpa's manner was somewhat proud and distant, but it turned out that he was on the defensive. He had visited London and possibly Edinburgh in 1782, but his English might, by now, have been a little rusty. Anyway, he asked Corneliani if Mackenzie understood Italian, but on being assured by the latter that he spoke French, his manner changed to one of great politeness. They had a long conversation on a multitude of very interesting subjects connected with the medical profession and the whole visit lasted two hours. Scarpa, when told that Mackenzie's interests lay in Surgery rather than Medicine, was very complimentary about surgery in England. It was, he said much more profoundly understood in England than in France. He gave Mackenzie particulars of his experiments in the treatment of aneurysm, a condition much more common in 1816 than nowadays, and also of his method of operating.

Scarpa seemed to be well acquainted with the museum of the Hunter brothers which he would visit when in this country and Mackenzie was able to tell him that William's museum was then in Glasgow and John's had been bought by the British Government and that his old teacher, Abernethy and also Lawrence, who was something of an ophthalmologist, gave lectures in the museum on Surgery and Comparative Anatomy respectively, illustrating them with reference to the preparations therein. When in London, Scarpa had spoken with John Hunter about his dissections of the olfactory nerves. He published a description of this work in 1789. Other famous names which cropped up in their conversation were Astley Cooper, Wishart of Edinburgh (who had translated Scarpa's book on Hernia into English), Allan Burns of Glasgow and also some of his fellow-students in London, Percival Pott, John Hunter (again), Sheldon, Cruickshanks and Smith, the author of the *Flora Brittanica*. He did not recall meeting Abernethy who was a pupil of Pott.

The subject of Ophthalmology was brought up and Scarpa told Mackenzie that he was about to bring out a new edition of his book on Diseases of the Eye and, whilst on the subject, he mentioned Wardrop's work on Fungus Haematodes and also his observations on the evacuation of the aqueous humour in ophthalmia. He added that he had asked his colleague Morizzi to give this form of treatment a trial. As we shall see those cases which responded well, were not suffering from true ophthalmia, but it is interesting to note the interest taken in this new approach.

After giving his guest coffee, Scarpa showed Mackenzie round his property which contained a wine-press, vines and fruit trees and showed him the magnificent view of the vast Plain of Lombardy from his house. Scarpa, in the course of conversation, guessed wrongly Mackenzie's age. He was, of course, still only twenty-five, but it was said that he looked older as he was prematurely bald and later became grey earlier than normal. Mackenzie does not seem to have been put out over this mistake. His description of Scarpa was complimentary. He wrote, 'He has been an elegant man in his appearance, and still preserves a dignified and gentleman-like look. He wears a long beard, up queue, a broad-brimmed silk hat, and a long coat. I have seldom been more highly pleased, in every respect, than I was with the reception I received from this celebrated man.' In his turn, Scarpa thanked Mackenzie again and again for his visit. Scarpa was, at this time, 69 years old.

A few days later, whilst walking in Pavia with Corneliani and De Antoni, the conversation turned upon religion and Mackenzie confessed to having some doubts about Calvinism. De Antoni asked keenly whether he found more satisfaction in the Catholic faith, but Mackenzie answered in the negative. Whereupon his friend argued considerably in its favour, recalling that Martin Luther on his death-bed had confessed that the Catholic religion was the most secure. Mackenzie however, remained a Protestant., He left Pavia for Genoa on 18th August by coach and found himself in the company of an Englishman called Paul Gooch, who wore moustaches and looked like an Italian, and also two Italians, one a maker of printing ink and one the director of a theatre. They were perturbed to learn that an English nobleman had been robbed on this road some eight days before at 8.00 a.m. The road was, in fact, one of the worst in Italy for robbers and guards were posted at intervals along it. They arrived in Genoa on the 20th and were greatly impressed by the beauty of the town and the sea.

Gooch and Mackenzie struck up a friendship and explored the town together. Mackenzie visited the Civil Hospital and the Hospital for Incurables. Many in the latter were mentally ill and some were even chained to their beds. Along with Gooch and the Italian theatre director, he took a boat out into the bay and made for a galley. They could see the slaves chained to the oars and guarded by Piedmontese soldiers, but, not surprisingly, they were not allowed aboard. They did, however, board a British brig bound for Malta, and later a Greek ship.

On 23rd August, he left Genoa in a small boat bound for Leghorn in the company of a Spanish courier bound for Rome. After three days he left Leghorn in the company of a Mr Richard Hey Sharp, an architect, who was going to study in Rome, by Cabriolet. Mr Sharp, at one point, handed Mackenzie a pistol in view of the suspicious-looking men who were lurking in the darkness beside the road. As the robbers usually went about in parties of eight or ten, Mackenzie pointed out the impropriety of using pistols on the Italian roads. Nevertheless, he kept it until they reached Pisa.

Like all self-respecting tourists, they climbed the leaning Tower. Sharp took a professional interest in the angle of deviation and pronounced his view that the inclination was artificial and the design of the architect. Mackenzie duly visited the hospital and saw Professor Vacca operate for the stone. The Hospital only contained about one hundred and seventy patients and there was no Museum of Anatomy and little opportunity for dissecting. In spite of this, there were two hundred students in Pisa studying Medicine. Rather characteristically, Mackenzie puzzled a lot over the leaning Tower of Pisa and came to the same conclusion as Sharp since it was built in an age when oddity was studied at least as much as elegance.

He left Pisa on 28th August *en route* for Florence, but was held up at Empoli by the unreasonable stubbornness of a horse which would not pull the cabriolet. So Mackenzie and an Italian fellow-traveller walked on to the next village and hired another cabriolet. In Florence, he duly visited the hospital and also went to visit the relatives of Mascagni, the late Professor of Anatomy who had died one year previously. He was famous for his illustrations of the anatomy of the human body. In the Museo di Fisico, he saw some very fine wax casts of various parts of the body and some mercurial preparations which he pronounced inferior to those of William Hunter. It was a remarkable museum, containing many wax models of insects, birds, fishes, reptiles, corals, seeds, plants, etc., which he described as the most perfect imitations in wax he had ever seen and was repeatedly at a loss to know whether they were not real. There were also fossil remains, mummies and casts of the inside of caverns containing dead and half-eaten bodies.

On 3rd September, he left Florence *en route* for Rome. He spent the night at Siena. At supper, the driver, on espying two ladies of easy virtue, asked Mackenzie which he would prefer. Courtesy apparently demanded that the visitor should have first choice even in such matters. As they skirted the Lago Bolsena, Mackenzie likened it to Loch Lomond. He deemed the people in this area very indolent and was very depressed by the large numbers of beggars and of robbers – anything but industry and labour. There were monks and priests all over the place also.

On 8th September they entered Rome. Mackenzie went almost at once to see the sights of ancient Rome. In the Forum, he remarked that 'some oxen lay in the Forum whose tinkling bells caused the only sound he heard in the place where the eloquence of Cicero once met the air'. In the Pantheon he saw a child in convulsions in front of a statue of the Virgin and the people round about praying for its deliverance.

Three days after arrival, he went to visit the Hospital of S. Spirito with its two hundred patients. He also saw the Foundling Hospital which had a rotating basket in its front door. The child was placed in the basket and the latter rotated into the hospital without opening the door. On 13th September, news came through that Lord Exmouth had destroyed Algiers, but Mackenzie makes no special observations on this in his Diary. The following day there was an important ceremony in Rome, the beatification of S. Alphonso Marco di Signori Napolitana. St Peter's was decorated with pictures illustrating the miracles of the new saint, in one of which he was depicted as being raised in the air. This apparently happened three times in front of many witnesses. Mass was said in St Peter's and many cardinals arrived in their coaches. There were priests and monks everywhere. In the afternoon, the Pope came to St Peter's to perform the beatification. Six beautiful black horses drew him along and he was preceded by a priest on a white mule bearing the ensign of the cross.

Before he left Rome, Mackenzie bought a copy of the prayer which was addressed to the statue of the Virgin in the Pantheon. It was here that he saw the girl in convulsions and whenever he went there, he saw a crowd kneeling before the Virgin. On 21st September, he left Rome and it was an anxious time. The fore horse fell in the street apparently from weakness and had to be left behind. They had two coachmen apparently, one with a broken nose and a face depicting desperate villainy and the other with one eye only and a face of low cunning. Between Rome and Albano, two fellows overtook them bringing with them a replacement for the fore horse. Mackenzie and the others walked for a bit, but those in the carriage were very alarmed by the appearance of the four. Accordingly, at Albano they obtained the services of one of the Pope's Dragoons. They arrived safely at Velletri and it transpired that the coachman was in debt and the three other suspicious looking characters were his creditors and felt they should keep him in sight!

At Gaeta, they took a boat and went sightseeing. Unfortunately, they took too long and arrived back after midnight. The law did not allow anybody to land without special permission. However, after one and a half hours they were permitted to land, but they had made up their minds that they would sleep on the boat. The time passed agreeably enough since a Frenchman on board amused them with his attempts to speak Italian and an Italian with his attempts to speak French. The Italian, in fact, laughed all the time, but an Englishman in the company scolded a Milanese gentleman for his inability to clear up the difficulty. There was a Spanish-American on board who spoke French, Italian and English and had visited Glasgow. He knew some friends of Mackenzie's there.

The Kingdom of Naples seems to have been full of rules and regulations, for at Capua the Englishman had to pose as a military captain in order to pass through the city gate since it was before daybreak. They arrived in Naples on 25th September and had their first sight of Vesuvius. The next day a miracle was due to be completed in the cathedral. This was the liquefaction of the blood of St Jornarius which had been in process for a week. Mackenzie went to the cathedral at 11.00 a.m., and saw the blood in a small bottle. It was obviously liquid. The devotees were allowed to kiss the bottle. Mackenzie formed a poor opinion of Naples. It bore every mark of a badly-governed town, he thought. There were many soldiers, crowds of priests and monks and multitudes of beggars. There was much splendour, but also the most shocking misery.

In the library of the Academia Reale, he saw some of the burnt manuscripts taken from Herculaneum which he described as resembling exactly burnt sticks. He watched the unfolding of one which, when it seemed ready to tear, had a pellicle of skin attached to it on one side. Priests did all the other work on the manuscripts such as transcribing, filling up vacancies, printing and publishing. Twelve completed works were by Philodemus upon a variety of subjects such as music, rhetoric, vice and virtue and Mackenzie began to make a list of the titles when he was told that this was not allowed without special permission. One other manuscript, that of Epicurus on the subject of nature, had been completed and Mackenzie watched the priests at work on others. Missing words were written in red, the readable words being transcribed in black. Apparently they burned the paper to a cinder whereupon the letters stood out on the blackness of the charred paper.

The next day, Mackenzie went to the ancient city of Pompeii and found the experience entrancing. He found the Temple to Aesculapius, an apothecary's shop with the sign of the serpent, and a house which he supposed to be that of a physician since there was an altar over which was the figure of an old man and at the sides, the figures of two serpents. He also saw the room of a surgeon which had been found complete with its instruments and another with a marble counter on which were the marks of cups. The guide maintained that this must have been a café, but Mackenzie took this with a grain of salt.

After leaving Pompeii, he descended to Herculaneum where there was nothing to be seen except the well, the digging of which gave rise to the discovery of Herculaneum, but many relics were to be seen in the Museum of Portici. Excavations had been begun more than one hundred years previously. The following day, Sunday, 29th September, Mackenzie left Naples at 6.00 a.m., and walked to Resina. He hired a mule and set off to climb Vesuvius. He saw the scars left by the latest eruption in 1810 and later the cinders of the famous eruption in A.D. 79. This eruption was recorded by the younger Pliny from eye-witness accounts. His uncle, the elder Pliny, had been killed apparently by suffocation from the ash when, as Admiral of the Roman Fleet, he had gone to assist the stricken people.

Remarkably, they came on a house of a monk who had made a garden on earth formed of cinders. They also saw some trees seven years of age thriving well. In the distance, the scars of the 1794 eruption could be seen. Finally, he had to leave the mule and proceed on foot. This became increasingly difficult due to the moving cinders, but he was helped by a long staff and duly reached the old crater at 11.10 a.m. The smoke was rising under his feet and the cinders felt hot. There were two newer craters further on and there was a slight eruption of lava as they watched. Mackenzie wrote in his Diary, 'I stopped at some distance to observe the stream of lava and I was struck with astonishment at the sublimity and novelty of such a sight. A stream of fluid mineral matter gleaming before me and moving slowly down the side of the mountain.' He approached it and, along with the guide, tried to look into the crater, but the heat was too much for him and he contented himself with pushing his staff into the stream of lava and watching it burning.

On the following day, he visited several grottoes, particularly interesting being the Grotto del Cane which had a small hole in the rock at one side. An old man put the head of his dog into this hole whereupon it began to breathe with difficulty and in a little more than a minute had a convulsion and apparently expired. However, it was promptly thrown outside and revived completely in another minute. An old woman lowered a lighted candle into the hole and it was immediately extinguished. Mackenzie did not, however, attempt to explain what particular gas was responsible.

Close to Naples, Mackenzie visited the Baths of Nero. He entered the grotto, but soon found it too hot and returned. An old man, however, went right to the end and came back with a pitcher of hot water in which they were able to boil two eggs.

On Wednesday, 2nd October, 1816, William Mackenzie left Naples and turned his face towards home again.

Looking up Queen Street from Argyle Street in 1794. From *Views and Notes of Glasgow in Former Times*, Allan and Ferguson, Publishers 1847. There is some evidence that James Mackenzie lived in the first house on the left behind the old farm buildings. Copied by the Author.

CHAPTER 5

The Grand Tour: Rome and Paris

MACKENZIE seems to have had a flair for entertaining himself with his fellow-passengers. This time he had for company two Bavarians, a Swiss and two Italians. Of the latter, one was called Albertolli and the other was a gentleman from Parma where Parmesan cheese is produced. Mackenzie refers to him as the Parmigiano and, on one occasion, the 'Formaggio Parmigiano' in a frivolous moment. He amused Mackenzie by stating that he believed the Bavarians had three wives and that the English did not believe in Christ. Four days later, he was back in Rome.

One of his first pleasures in Rome, true to tradition, was to have a cup of tea. The last time he had tasted tea was the night of his arrival in Paris on 9th May, five months before. Two days after his arrival, he left Rome for Florence and wrote in his Diary, 'Probably never again to behold the fragments of the once mistress of the world.' On the way at Montefiasconi, the coachman's boots were stolen and another man's watch was stolen so that they were delayed and, when they stopped for the night at Novella, Mackenzie found his room full of fleas. Accordingly, he spent the night in the coach in the stable where he was later joined by a French fellow-traveller for the same reason.

When they reached Siena, they were unlucky enough to be involved in an earthquake. Mackenzie was in the main street of the town watching a man selling roasted chestnuts when the shock came. Several buildings were badly damaged, but none of their party was hurt and they went on to Florence.

On the way from Florence to Pisa, he travelled with an apothecary who told him about the famous Italian anatomist, Mascagni. He came from Siena and was called to Florence by Bonaparte and later to Paris merely so that he could become acquainted with a famous personage. He stayed with Napoleon until the latter came to Milan. He was said to be an opium addict and consumed sixty grs. per day.

From Pisa, he journeyed to Leghorn where he decided to travel as far as Nice by sea. This was to prove a very adventurous journey and a frustrating one. On 16th October, they spent a day waiting for their felucca to sail, but the wind was contrary and there was rain in the afternoon. The latter continued all through the night and they did not sail until the 18th at 7.00 a.m. The weather was very unkind and the wind died down in the late afternoon forcing them to row until sunset. Later that evening, a wind got up and they made for Porto Venere where they stayed all night. It was very cold and there was no bed for the passengers. The weather continued stormy and they crossed the Gulf of Spezia back to Lerici. There they were told to stay until the weather improved, but Mackenzie found out that this was the home of the owners of the felucca and they wanted to spend the day there.

On 20th October, they left Lerici and encountered a stormy side-wind as soon as they left the Gulf of Spezia and entered the open sea. The rain came on and they had to row again in order to reach Sestri by 6.00 p.m. The next day, on passing a small village west of Sestri called Lavagna, they were struck by a thunderstorm and they made for Chiavari. The master and two of the crew succeeded in landing and attaching a rope to the stern of the felucca, but they could not drag her ashore. The felucca was alternately filled with water and driven violently against the shore so that an elderly member of the crew was engaged in bailing all the time. A boy kept crying and a forty-year old Roman peasant, the only other passenger, prayed for assistance. The storm became worse and worse and finally Mackenzie decided that the felucca could not survive the storm. Accordingly, he decided to jump into the sea and pull himself ashore by the rope. He jumped from the stern after saying some comforting words to the boy and the peasant and was startled by the depth of the sea. However, he was ashore in a few seconds with the aid of a large wave which swept him towards the rope. They dragged the felucca ashore and, as luck would have it, the storm speedily abated. In a few hours, Mackenzie reported that he was again ready to tempt the dangers of the deep. The only casualty seems to have been his watch which declined to go after being immersed in water, but he declared that he judged the time by the Ave Marias.

The next day they were still storm-stayed at Chiavari, but at sunrise the following day, they were off again and reached Genoa in the darkness. Three days later they were in Nice. The whole trip, which was probably in the nature of a short-cut, took ten days, but, of course, Mackenzie may have used this means of transport from choice. In fact, he seems to have been very fond of the country considering that he was a city dweller and it makes one wonder whether he spent some of his early days in the country. He was certainly well acquainted with the Loch Lomond area since he referred to the Smollet Monument in Renton and likened some parts of the Continent to Loch Lomond and Ben Lomond. He was also apparently well versed in the various crops which he saw and took a great interest in the ploughing activities. Whether he could swim or not, one cannot tell, but it is unlikely that he would have jumped into the sea at Chiavari if he were a non-swimmer. The Loch Lomond area was, of course, a favourite location for coach drives from Glasgow and he may have been taken there for the day. His father may also have taken his children to the district for a holiday as he seems to have been financially well off. There is another reference in his Diary written about the road between Montmellian and

St Jean. 'Feelings renewed of youthful days.' One of his references to agriculture in Switzerland has an amusingly pedantic sound, 'Man ploughing with a mule and cow and a man as a leader. The cow did not seem to regard the mule with much affection and the man was pulling more than either.' It conjures up a nice rustic picture, but does not help one to decide how much country lore Mackenzie possessed, although his future wife was an Elgin farmer's daughter.

On 29th October, Mackenzie left Nice in a carriage for Marseilles. At this point, he observed in his Diary that he thought the manners of the Continental natives were primitive and there was a familiarity between the different ranks, contrasted with the manners of the English. The following day, he stopped in the forenoon at Cannes which he described as a small seaport town. He noticed a large amount of porphyry on the road.

On arrival at Aix-en-Provence, he espied a carriage going to Lyons and gave up the idea of going to Marseilles. The next day he was in Avignon and saw the famous Bridge with its middle resting on an island and unfinished. He makes no reference to anybody dancing on it. Apart from stops for meals, Mackenzie travelled for three days without real rest and arrived at Lyons on 5th November. It rained excessively here and Mackenzie would have liked to move on to Paris, but he did not have the ready cash at the moment. Accordingly, he paid the half-fare and ruefully wrote in his Diary that, if he only had another Napoleon, he could reach Paris. His spirits sank very low and did not rise when, on going to a café for hot coffee, he read the barometer needle which pointed to 'Grande Pluie'. He wandered about the town waiting for money to come from Paris and, as usual, visited the hospital. He also went to the theatre and saw 'La Pie Voleuse' and so the time passed until a bill for two hundred francs arrived by the postman six days after his arrival.

The weather was beginning to be cold and at Palise, Mackenzie bought a pair of fur gloves. At this point he was consulted by a Frenchman in the company who was anxious to know whether he could have caught a venereal infection from sleeping in a dirty bed in Lyons. Mackenzie does not record his advice.

Three days after leaving Lyons, a wheel broke and a little later two wolves crossed the road in front of them. The passengers all shouted as loudly as possible to scare them off. The next day snow fell and it was only 16th November. The following day he arrived in Paris and wrote, 'I return to the Metropolis of a foreign land, of a country for many years at open warfare with my own, and whose inhabitants carry in their heart a rancour which perphaps never can be rooted out against even the very name of an Englishman. I return to that capital as I would to my home.' This was a great compliment to the medical fraternity in Paris who had made him welcome.

This visit to Paris was to be a much lengthier one than the last one but, like the latter, was to be dedicated to work. The first day, however, he settled himself in the Hôtel de L'Estrapade, wrote home to Rainy and sought out his old friend Kontzofsky. The next day saw him hard at work at the Hôtel Dieu watching Dupuytren and other surgeons at work. One of the latter was a humourist in a black velvet cap called Pelletan who lectured on Lithotomy. There was an eclipse of the sun that day. The next day, however, he went to the Hôpital de la Pitié and arranged to start dissecting. He was able to purchase a subject and began with the muscles of the abdomen on 26th November. Each day in his Diary he recorded the parts of the body which he had dissected and it is obvious that he was deeply engrossed in this work. This is understandable since the opportunities to dissect in Great Britain at that time were very scarce. In the Anatomy rooms he made friends with a Dr Walker, surgeon in the 71st Regiment. This famous Scottish Regiment had fought at Waterloo and were reputed to have fired the last shot with a captured French cannon which they turned round and fired at the retreating French. The Regiment in 1816 were doing duty in the Army of Occupation and Walker was making the most of his opportunities by studying Anatomy. His friends kept writing to him. George Oswald Sym, a friend from the Faculty of Divinity kept him informed of the riots in London in December 1816. Armour wrote about going into partnership with Mackenzie and renting a shop and Rainy kept him informed about his personal affairs, including news of the death of one of his few relatives, his cousin, Mrs Burgess. It turned out that she left £75 in her Will to Mackenzie.

It was not long, however, before he found his way back to the St Louis hospital to hear his old favourite Alibert. He was lecturing on Cancer and the terminology sounds strange to modern ears. Included were varieties such as fungus, tenebrans, globular, anthracine, tuberous, etc. Meantime, he was dissecting away at the Pitié hospital. On Christmas Eve, however, he went to Notre Dame for half an hour, but thought it not so fine as some of the cathedrals he had seen in Italy. On Christmas Day, however, he celebrated the holiday by dissecting the nerves of the orbit. Two days later he recorded that he had broken a pair of scissors and the *pot-de-chambre*, but gives no further details and leaves posterity wondering whether this was in the course of his dissections or elsewhere.

Like all Scots in 1816, he waxed somewhat sentimental and philosophical on New Year's Eve. He wrote in his Diary, 'And now the year 1816 is about to close. I have had many opportunities during the last twelve months of improving myself in professional knowledge and of enlarging my views of mankind. I have visited no fewer than eight of the capital cities of Europe. I have had occasion of seeing and listening to the first masters of the Art of Surgery in England, in France and in Italy. Some circumstances have given me so much pleasure that I must remember them throughout life with envious feelings of the past. I must ever remember the Alps, Scarpa, Rome and Vesuvius as four of the grandest objects on which my eyes ever rested. My opportunities have not been improved as they might have been.

Many have been the contests between my evil and my good genius; the former has oft prevailed and oftener thrown a damping influence on my exertions.'

'I turn my thoughts to this night last year and feel gratitude towards Heron for the good wishes he so fervently expressed for my success. I am fond of praise, I seldom deserve it. I am almost never favoured with it.' 'By this time next year, I expect to be in Glasgow and deeply engaged in a course of lectures on Anatomy. Years have sometimes the semblance of long periods when we look forwards on to futurity. When we look back they appear as an hour.' He then quoted in Latin, a passage which translated means, 'Beside the River Hyspanius, which flows from part of Europe into the Black Sea, Aristotle says that certain small animals are born which live for one day. Of these, therefore, one which has died at the eighth hour, has died at an advanced age; but one which has died at sunset, has died in extreme old age; all the more so if it is also at Midsummer. Compare our longest life with eternity; we are found to be almost in the same brief span as those small animals.'

On 2nd January, 1817, he arranged with Bogros, the prosector, to assist him at the rate of sixty francs per month and he began to help Mackenzie two days later. His life, however, was not all work and no play for the following evening he went with a new friend called Norvicky to a gaming-house in the Palais Royal. He took stock of his surroundings with some displeasure and described the faces of several people who were professed gamesters. One young man increased his stake every time he lost and a middle-aged man lost considerably and then paced about the room muttering at every new loss till he finally hurried out. There were, he wrote, many dull unmeaning faces seemingly belonging to men incapable of any higher enjoyment. In short, it is safe to assume that William Mackenzie, from Presbyterian Scotland, did not approve of gambling.

There was a holiday on 21st January, the anniversary of the death of Louis XVI. Bells rang all day and Mackenzie remarked that this made the day more like a fête than a day of mourning, but the Parisians did not seem to pay much attention to it either way. The next day, he went to Notre Dame which was dressed up for ceremonies expiatory of the death of Louis XVI. About this time, he began to ponder on his future and he commenced to wonder whether he might not lecture on Anatomy in Paris. Meantime, two friends, John Couper and Moses Buchanan arrived from Glasgow and his friend, Dr Walker, who had been dissecting at the Pitié, called to say that his mother was ill and he had to go home to Stirling. Mackenzie was very sorry to see him go.

On Sunday, 16th February, he witnessed 'Dimanche Gras' during which an ox decorated with garlands processed through the streets accompanied by masked figures on foot and on horseback. The festivities went on for days and Mackenzie remarked that the French seemed to devote themselves with greater enthusiasm and make pleasure the business of everyday. It sounds as if he did not approve of such frivolities.

He finished his dissection on 25th February and so he had spent three months less a day on this work. When he obtained a second subject, the porter in the dissecting room complained that he would raise an infection if he kept it as long as he did the last one!

On 7th March, he spent the evening with Couper and Buchanan and they met several times, laughing over old stories. Both these worthies were about Mackenzie's age and both were to become distinguished as surgeons to the Glasgow Royal Infirmary, Couper was to be an expert in Materia Medica and Buchanan in Anatomy, but in 1816 all three were in their twenties and their lives lay before them. There was a sad, but interesting little interlude when the elephant at the Jardin des Plantes died. Mackenzie went along to see what was happening and found Blainville with a crowd of Cuvier's dissectors, dissecting the elephant's muscles whilst an artist drew them. Many men were standing at the side of the abdomen and Mackenzie confessed that the scene recalled to his mind the examination of Gulliver by the Lilliputians.

He went to the Veterinary Museum at Alfort with his friends, Couper and Buchanan and saw, amongst other exhibits, the heart of a sow which had been ruptured during a paroxysm of hydrophobia and the jawbone of a horse which had been fractured when it had bitten on a hard object during the same disease. Couper and Buchanan also helped with his dissections and they went to the Opera Comique to hear 'Wallace or Le Maestro Ecossais'.

On 16th April, James Armour, along with Wallace and Maclurg arrived and he and Mackenzie had long talks. Mackenzie mentioned an idea he had of lecturing on Medical Jurisprudence in Glasgow. Armour thoroughly approved of this scheme which did, in fact, come to fruition. Orfila had been giving lectures on this subject and Mackenzie had been attending them. The lectures he had been attending on Anatomy by Marjolin had also come to an end and it was time for Mackenzie to leave Paris again. Before doing so, he went to the Théâtre Francais to see L'Avare and Les Fouberis de Scapin. He spied a young man in the pit who was affected by violent convulsive movements of his left hand and arm when anything on the stage particularly pleased him. The convulsion ceased when he looked at the stage through an opera glass and Mackenzie concluded that he suffered from chorea.

He was there again, one week later, when he saw his first French tragedy, Semiram. The acting, he thought, was only second rate.

He left Paris, en route for Strasbourg, on 17th July, 1817.

CHAPTER 6

The Grand Tour: Vienna, Prague and Paris

MACKENZIE was now making for Vienna and this episode in his tour was going to prove to be a very important one. He was about to learn about Ophthalmology in greater detail and so his life-work began.

He, therefore, trundled on towards Strasbourg, noting on the way that the Prussian soldiers he saw were handsome fellows, but the French soldiers, in general, were either very like dancing masters or cut-throats! On 22nd July, five days after leaving Paris, two hundred and ninety-seven miles away, he reached Strasbourg. After he had been in Germany for three days, he admitted that, in all conscience, he could say that he could not understand a word of spoken German. This, however, was soon to be remedied and he became an accomplished German speaker although he always seems to have preferred to converse in French, if possible. When he reached Munich and went to visit the hospital, the director showed him round and they were able to speak a little French, but also some Latin.

On a visit to the palace of the King of Bavaria, he was interested to find a small piece of sculpture in the chapel with a latin inscription on it which stated, 'This image was the companion of the exiled and imprisoned Mary Queen of Scots. It would have been with her at her execution if she had taken it with her.' In Munich he went to visit the famous Soemerring who spoke English with him and told him that he had studied in Edinburgh and had also visited Glasgow. He knew many of the medical men of the day in Britain and praised Allan Burns, the Glasgow anatomist, Astley Cooper, the London surgeon and anatomist, and Abernethy, Mackenzie's old chief. He did not think so much of Sir William Adams and regarded Saunders, the founder of Moorfields, as something of a quack. He also referred to the serious lack of dissecting in Britain and cheered Mackenzie by telling him of the many opportunities for study and practical anatomy he would find in Vienna. At this time, Soemerring was puzzling over the structure of the macula lutea and finally came to the conclusion it was a hole.

On 30th July, Mackenzie left Munich for Straubing, but not before going to the theatre twice.

Whether Mackenzie grew tired of trundling across Europe in a carriage at a rate of some ten miles per hour or not, one cannot tell, but when he reached Vilshofen, he boarded a Danube boat bound for Linz and Vienna.

'THE UNDERTAKER'S ARMS, OR A CONSULTATION
OF PHYSICIANS'

A caricature by Hogarth. The three figures at the top of this design which is
done in the style of heraldry, are Chevalier Taylor, the oculist (a trade denoted
by the eye in the head of his cane); 'Crazy Sally' Mapp, the bone-setter; and
Spot Ward, whose birth mark is shown. The twelve figures in the center are
caricatures of quacks of Hogarth's time. Hogarth's inscription to this picture
follows the conventions of heraldry, 'The company of Undertakers bearth,
sable, an urinal, proper between twelve quack heads of the second, and twelve
cane heads, or, consultant . . . with this motto, *Et plurima mortis imago*. The
general image of death.'

Reproduced from *Devils, Drugs and Doctors* by Howard W. Haggard, 1929
William Heinemann Ltd.

GEORG JOSEF BEER
1763–1821

ANTONIO SCARPA
1747–1832

The two famous continental teachers who greatly influenced William Mackenzie.

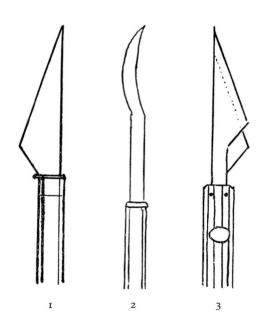

1   2   3

Three Cataract Knives in use in William Mackenzie's time.
1. Beer's (Mackenzie's Favourite).   2. Pelliet's (1785).
3. Jaeger's Double-bladed. The second blade was slid up if the first incision were
unsuccessful.
*From 'Historical and Critical Remarks on the Operation for the Cure of Cataract' by
Alex. Watson, Edinburgh Medical and Surgical Journal No. 165, 1845.*

He was interested to see that boats going in the opposite direction, i.e. upstream, were dragged along by twenty or thirty horses. This trip by the river was one of the highlights of the Continental journey and was on a par with the ascent of the Mont Cénis pass. Mackenzie was entranced by the scenery and in his Diary he described it with a lucidity and a beautiful phraseology which were to characterise his later writings. 'Every step about Passau presents a new landscape which needs not the art of Poussin to render it sublime, unless perhaps in the eye of the artificial Painter or pretended connoisseur,' he wrote. The journey was enlivened by a German who sang tunes out of a book which reminded Mackenzie of Scottish Psalm tunes and at other times made everybody laugh.

The diary continues, 'Every little turn which the river takes persuades me more and more that it is on the Danube and its banks that the landscape painter ought to study and the admirer of nature's beauties to wander. Is that a real boat which I saw by the shore, is that a real cottage, or are these objects miniatures which some fanciful inhabitant of the country has set down to amuse the passing traveller and to make him believe that the Danube is broader, its banks more wonderful than they really are? I see a man enter the cottage: I see various animals all in proportion, and am persuading myself that these seeming shrubs which bend beneath the wind are lofty and wide spreading oaks. If these scenes are so beautiful, although there be not a ray of sunshine, but on the contrary the whole horizon presents a uniform cloud, how would they strike the sense in one of these days when the sun shines in such lustre and when the sky is so ethereal that the most common scenes of the country, those to which we have been long and daily accustomed enchant us by their beauty and make every little nerve within us beat with joy? The Danube takes a sudden turn and we are on all sides so surrounded with mountains that for a moment we fancy ourselves on a lake, but the rapid stream and the labouring oar soon undeceive us and bring into view the windings of the river with new objects on its banks to surprise and please us. I have often seen that on visiting some scene celebrated for its beauties, the beauties were to be sought for and the spectator to be reasoned into admiration. It cannot be so with him who visits the ever-varied banks of the Danube. The Monks who have so well known to appreciate the beauties of France and Italy and even to appropriate them to themselves have not overlooked these romantic banks. Here, a little chapel or a hermitage is half hid on a shaded hill, where the foot of man no longer wanders. There, a stately convent rises on the very summit of a mountain as if it were a temple of priestly pride, but the funds have been turned to other uses and the Monastery is deserted.' So Mackenzie sang the praises of the River Danube. He does not mention its blueness and Herr Strauss was not yet born. Perhaps nobody else regarded it as blue and it was claimed by the romantics that it only looked blue when one was in love. So far as we know, William Mackenzie was not in that happy state in 1817.

D

It took the boat two days to reach Linz and shortly afterwards Mackenzie notes, rather drily, that the sailors, on passing a considerable whirlpool, used to pray for the safety of the passengers, but now they converted their prayer into a demand for money from them. Near the whirlpool, they saw the castle reputed to have been Richard Coeur de Lion's prison. They arrived in Vienna on 5th August, i.e. four days after leaving Vilshofen and, in the evening, Mackenzie went to the circus. On the following day, he took an introductory letter which Perret had given him to Dr Tjallongii and later Arnott's introductory letter to Professor Georg Josef Beer. The latter expressed his admiration for Arnott. Beer was one of the most distinguished of the Austrian ophthalmologists and, as the Austrian Medical School had an international reputation, it could fairly be said that he was one of the world authorities on Ophthalmology at the time. He was Professor of Ophthalmology in Vienna, a post which he had at that time held for five years, but the Medical School itself was founded in 1745 by Van Swieten and the Ophthalmic School five years later by Nicholas Josef Pallucci from Florence. The first public teacher, however, was Joseph Barth who began lecturing in 1773. He had four distinguished pupils, Beer, Prochaska, Schmidt and Santerelli. Beer became the first special Professor for Diseases of the Eye and the founder of modern Ophthalmology in Europe. One of his pupils, Jäger, became his assistant and then special Professor of Ophthalmology to the Josephinum Academy, the students being surgeons training to be medical officers in the Austrian Army and the patients members of the armed forces and their families.

These then, were the ophthalmic clinics in Vienna in 1817 which were at Mackenzie's disposal and he made full use of them. The University Clinic had opened a new theatre for operations and lecturing the year before and in it had placed busts of the Emperor Francis I and of Andreas von Stift, the chief medical officer. To these were added portraits of famous medical men. Here were assembled in time, Barth, Prochaska, Rust, Soemmering, Richter, Schmidt, Fisher, Quadri, Von Walter, Graefe, Jünken and Von Ammon. Young William Mackenzie could not know that, in the fullness of time, his own portrait was to hang there with the others, but this was the list which Dr W. R. Wilde of Dublin, (Oscar's father) was to record in 1841 in an article which he published in the *Dublin Journal of Medical Science* and he sent a reprint to Mackenzie although he would know all about his portrait being there.

It has often been conjectured when exactly Mackenzie turned his attention to Ophthalmology. The question cannot be answered with certainty, but there is no doubt about the influence which Beer had on him. Curiously enough, the first operation he saw done by Beer was a forceps delivery for a woman with eclampsia, but later he attended his course on operative surgery and, under his guidance, did his first extraction of cataract on the cadaver. His description of this experience is interesting and will strike a sympathetic chord in the hearts of many an ophthalmologist. In his diary he records that on 3rd October, 'It came my turn to operate for cataract in Beer's course. He put the knife into my left hand and desired me to operate on the right eye of a head which was stuck up before me, telling me at the same time to remember his direction to point the knife at first towards the iris. I took the knife and glad to see that I held it with a steady hand, I plunged in through not merely the cornea, but through the iris into the bargain. Not discomposed by this horrid blunder, I withdrew the knife a little and carried it tolerably well across the anterior chamber. Penetrating the internal side of the cornea, I came into contact, most unfortunately, with the side of the nose and gave the "patient" such a prick as would have made him dance a little if he had been alive. When the incision was completed, Beer pronounced it too small and ill-shaped. Of course it had to be enlarged with Daviel's scissors. Everyone agreed that in the living subject such an incision would be followed by an unsightly cicatrix.'

Four days later he made his second attempt again with the left hand and this time Beer pronounced it 'Ein schöner Schnitt'. After doing several other operations, he did his third extraction two weeks later and the same day met an Englishman called Gordon. This association was going to be important for them both and they soon struck up a friendship. Gordon, in spite of his Scottish name, was born in Middlesex, but graduated at Edinburgh University.

Mackenzie could not fail to be impressed by the comparison between arrangements for study and tuition in Vienna compared with those in his native Glasgow. Specialisation had begun on the Continent long before 1817 and in Britain the doctor was still expected to know all there was to know about everything. William Mackenzie subscribed to this view in part and carried on some general practice until the end of his life. In Vienna, he attended Hildenbrand's Clinique on Internal Diseases and described him as an ill-mannered-looking joking man. Later, when Gordon and Mackenzie visited Hildenbrand, the latter took Gordon for a Lower Saxon and Mackenzie for a Westphalian and, Mackenzie wrote in his Diary, was about to insult them, but when he heard that they were English and Scottish respectively, he was uncommonly polite. He does not attempt to explain the reasons for this odd behaviour. Mackenzie, however, did have a few criticisms. For example, when he tried to read Beer's *Leitfaden*, he found the introduction 'The greatest nonsense ever written'. He discussed this with Professor Frank of Wilma who explained that Beer belonged to a German sect who called themselves the philosophers of nature, but Frank said that they were not philosophers at all in his view and it was little wonder that Mackenzie could not understand him since many Germans were in the same state. Frank said that he admired Beer's power of diagnosis, but doubted the propriety of his division into stadia and momenta and his employment of bleeding in certain stadia and never after these had passed. Also, he found the cabinet of Natural History very disappointing and wrote, 'It is really amazing how such ill-prepared specimens could have been collected.' On the other hand, he had no complaints about Dr Bremser's collection of intestinal worms which had taken him eight years to complete and for which he said he had dissected fifty thousand animals!

When he went to the opening of the clinics of Hildenbrand, Boer and Beer, he made no comment on the first, apart from recording that he delivered an introductory lecture in Latin, but he recorded that Boer stood in the middle of the Delivery Room and 'havered' for ten minutes. Beer, he wrote, began Anatomy of the Eye.

Amongst his diversions, Mackenzie began to learn horseriding at the Cadet-Institute. The theatre, as previously, interested him greatly and he records seeing a pantomime in the Leopaldstadt Theatre, a performance of 'William Tell' at the Wien Theatre and also a circus. He found the Prater an exciting place somewhat like the Champs Elysees as already recorded, only bigger and finer. He lists 'Jews and Turks – Philosophers – Dreaming Smokers – Waltzers – Pretty Women – Carriages and Horses – Pedestrians – Music – Coffee Houses and all kinds of amusements'. He also visited an artillery review on one occasion and he had an interesting experience in September when he went to see a tree about two hours' walk from Vienna which had been discovered four months previously to have the face of Jesus on it. Mackenzie was of the opinion that it had been carved on the tree when the latter was small. The devout, however, regarded it as a miracle and made it into a shrine. Near the tree was a spring of water in which the sick bathed, hoping for a cure. The crowds were becoming too great and Mackenzie records four days later that the police had cut the tree down. On 18th September, Mackenzie recorded that a colleague called Blömer cleaned his watch. It had apparently not recovered properly from its wetting off the coast of Italy and he had found it too expensive to have it repaired in France. By 11th September, he reported that he was making a little progress in speaking German, but he still preferred to use French when possible. He became very friendly with Gordon and the latter conceived the idea of publishing a foreign Medical Journal. This commended itself to Mackenzie and he promptly wrote to Corneliani asking if he would be willing to collaborate with them and contribute articles. This he readily accepted and so the Journal was born. Corneliani, however, complained bitterly that Mackenzie had not employed his article in the Journal at a later date. Later, they approached Jaeger, but his reply is not recorded.

Before he left Vienna, Mackenzie visited the Blinde-Anstalt for the training of the blind. He was very interested to note that they were able to give a concert and that they worked with a sort of Braille, i.e. they learned to read letters printed in relief on paper. Similarly, they had a history of the world and an almanack which they could study. They also learned to prick out a word with a pin and then feel the reverse side with their fingers. They were taught to distinguish coins by their weight and by the sound they made when falling and materials by the sound they made when bent. He observed some blind children who made see-saw movements most of the time and one boy who whirled himself round until he became giddy.

On 30th November, 1817, William Mackenzie left by coach at 8.00 a.m., bound for Prague which was then part of the Austro-Hungarian Empire. This was not a very comfortable journey for at times they had no beds in the inns and they slept on straw on the floor. They reached Prague five days after setting out. He found the Bohemian language impossible to understand which is hardly surprising.

His next stop was at Dresden and once more he met up with the mysterious Hodgkin. They had met in Vienna as well as in Paris and they seemed to get on very well together. Mackenzie, however, never gave any details of their conversation or of the letters which passed between them. It is tempting to think that he might have been the physician who described the disease which bears his name, but they never seem to have met at a clinic or hospital and at his first meeting with Hodgkin, Mackenzie calls him 'Lieutenant'. He must remain a mystery. The second last reference in the Diary is for 11th December when he records that they dined together out of Dresden. The name is spelt 'Hodgskin' this time, but at others it is spelt 'Hogskin' or 'Hoskin'. That night, Mackenzie went to the theatre where he saw the King of Saxony, who carried a muff, and his brothers and children. When he visited the hospital in Dresden, he saw the surgical work of Ohle and the medical work of Kreisig. The latter knew quite a lot about Glasgow and, as so often happened, Allan Burns, in particular. On 16th December, he went to a declamatory exhibition in the evening with Hodgkin and this is the last record of him in Mackenzie's diary. On 17th December, William Mackenzie left Dresden at 6.00 a.m., bound for Leipzig where he passed over the field of the battle. Two days later, he left *en route* for Berlin which he reached in another two days. Mackenzie was delighted with the appearance of the capital of Prussia singling out for special mention the Palace, the Linden Allee, the Brandenburg Gate, the soldiers and (once more) 'Such Women'. Finally, he wrote, 'One might imagine one was set down into a city of another world, inhabited by the Gods.' Strong words indeed! There was deep snow in Berlin and Mackenzie was greatly pleased by the sledges and the outriders. Blücher, he wrote, was a common-sense man, but a man of no culture.

He was disappointed with Walther's Museum, but judged it better than William Hunter's. He visited it with Professor Rudolphi, who had plans to make a Natural History Museum, on 31st December, when there was a 'Sausage Feast' and that evening, as was his wont on Hogmanay, he wrote a short soliloquy in his diary. 'And I am here in the capital of Prussia. Anatomy flies like a coy nymph from before me, and yet my eye is fixed upon her. What improvement have I made during the last year? I have gained some considerable knowledge in the manner of dissection, have attended somewhat to the treatment of the venereal disease, and was at least extremely interested in the study of medical jurisprudence. I have read with enthusiasm the works of Brichat. What I have gained in Ophthalmology is, I think, considerable. I have acquired some degree of facility in reading the medical authors of Germany. I have conversed with Soemmering, Himly, Beer, Prochaska, the younger Frank, Hildenbrandt, Gollis, Kreisig, Ohle, Bock, Rudolphi. I have formed friendships with Perret, Tjellingii, von Gohr, Gordon, Gire, Schackenwert, Bünger. The manner of conducting the clinique, I have learned from Hildenbrand.'

'The year 1818 approaches in clouds.'

On New Year's Day, Mackenzie was interested to hear that there were sermons being preached in all the Berlin churches since this would be going on in his native Glasgow too. He was impressed with Rust's words, but not his Ophthalmology. There were, however, puddles on the floor from baths which were constantly in the wards and, in one of these, he watched two men at one time. Remarkably, he saw two cases of skin-grafting in Graefe's clinic. Both had lost their noses, one a young woman from herpes and the other, a middle-aged man from syphilis.

Whilst in Berlin, Mackenzie proposed a visit to a Dr Wohlfart who was a magnetismer and a pupil of the famous Mesmer. He was told, however, that he made a secret of his manipulations and was therefore not accepted by the respectable. Mackenzie added, 'But has been tried seemingly by many from whom we would have expected better sense.' Berlin was the chief seat of Magnetism and it was believed there that the priests and priestesses of antiquity were under its influence.

William Mackenzie left Berlin at 6.00 a.m., on 6th January on his way to Paris once more. The next day, however, he was seized with colic and had to rest at Magdeburg. This is one of the few references to sickness he records and, apart from occasional travel-sickness (which is not surprising, considering the number of miles he covered in lurching carriages) and to colds in the head, he seems to have enjoyed excellent health all the time he was on the Continent.

When he reached Göttingen, he found Gordon and also letters from Corneliani and McQuahe and in the library there he met Blumerbach who reminisced about the Hunter Brothers and once more spoke favourably of Allan Burns, but was critical of Pott.

On his way to Mainz, Mackenzie was startled to find himself in the company of an actress who had baggage valued 150,000 gulden. He found Mainz filled with Austrian and Prussian troops. This part of Germany seems to have had some difficulty in deciding which side it was on. French manufacturers were allowed into Mainz, but the commerce was not reciprocal and the people of Mainz sided with the French. When he left on 22nd January, Mackenzie dined at Alzey. There he found that the Grand Duke of Damstadt had ordered the conscription of all the young men. The latter hoisted the tricolour at first, but as Mackenzie wrote, 'Wisely resigned their hostile passions to the dominion of Bacchus in the Alehouse.'

Mackenzie reached Paris on 29th January and sought out his friends. Gordon, Couper and Buchanan had all left, but a Dr Gibson was there and he soon ferretted out his old friend Walker. For a spell these two discussed a plan to lecture together on Anatomy, but this came to nothing. He did, however, obtain a cadaver and dissected the brain in Walker's Cabinet de le Pitié. This was followed by a dissection of the nerves of the body and whilst he was so engaged he reported that the Duke of Wellington had been shot at. He also joined Walker in plaster-cast making, just before he left Paris on 1st March.

Three days later, he sailed from Calais at 9.00 a.m., on board the *Lady Jane James* and landed at Dover at 4.00 p.m. A violent storm arose four hours later and the ship parted from the Downs. The next day Mackenzie set off for Ramsgate, walking the thirteen miles between Deal and the latter. He was in search of not only his own luggage, but also that of a Mr Knowles, who was worried about some documents in his writing case and whom Mackenzie had promised to help. *En route*, he saw a large number of wrecks and found out nothing about his luggage. At 6.00 p.m., he left Ramsgate with a heavy heart and at 6.00 a.m., the next day, he arrived in London.

Greyfriars Church and Inkle Factory Lane from *Sketches of the History of Glasgow.* Published by Robert Stewart & Company, Ingram Street, and *Glasgow Delineated.* Printed by the University Press 1827. The late Dr Leslie Buchanan was of the opinion that the old Eye Infirmary was housed in the building on the right. Copied by the Author.

CHAPTER 7

The London Venture

WILLIAM MACKENZIE was the proud possessor of several cases of books, instruments, dissections and specimens and, on arrival in London, wrote to the captain of the *Lady Jane James* in which his heavy luggage had crossed the Channel to learn of their whereabouts and meanwhile he went in search of his friend Arnott and found him in Golden Square. He took a room nearby in Queen Street and awaited developments.

The news of the *Lady Jane James* was bad. She was reported lost at sea. This must have been a severe blow, but at least some of his baggage was saved as he received a letter from the proprietors a week later to say that a Packet had landed his luggage at Ramsgate. So off he went to Sandwich to pay the duty.

He was still hankering after a career in Anatomy and, only four days after his arrival in London, he was looking at Bell's old dissecting rooms in Leicester Square along with his friend Arnott. The rent, however, was £150 per annum, too expensive for the young Mackenzie, but Sir Charles Bell was famous by now as the originator of the term 'Bell's Palsy' and was able to ask big prices.

However, he had been away from home for over two years and it was time to set his affairs in order in Glasgow. On 3rd April, having decided after much vacillation to settle in London, he left by coach for Edinburgh. He travelled all night and breakfasted at Ferrybridge in Yorkshire. He spent a night in Newcastle and arrived in Edinburgh at midnight on 6/7th April having passed through Berwick. This journey, therefore, took the best part of four days, but it would have taken nearly a week fifty years before. A new coach service, however, was introduced in 1788 by John Palmer. He built fast coaches and employed special horses to pull them. The men who changed the four horses *en route* cut the time taken to one minute with the help of specially designed harness which could be quickly dismantled and then reassembled. This was the time too when McAdam, the road-maker and Telford, the bridge-builder, improved the roads and travelling was becoming more of a pleasure. Travelling time was cut to forty-four hours and involved forty-five changes of horses.

Mackenzie's business did not take very long. He stayed with Rainy and settled up his affairs with him and his other friends and, in eight days set off again for Leith. This time he chose the other route to London, by sea. On 21st April, he embarked on the *Lord Wellington*. The journey was an eventful one because two days out they encountered a gale. The next day it was feared that the ship might become waterlogged and go down, but the captain sailed back to the Humber and they lay off Grimsby. There were some two hundred ships in the Humber and two were reported wrecked. There were certainly two wrecks visible off Spurn Head. All hands of one had been lost. After two days, they left the Humber, anchored off Yarmouth in the evening and off Lowestoft the following evening. The next day they reached London. Mackenzie was very impressed by the apple blossom and described Greenwich Hospital as perhaps the most imposing building he had ever seen. He spent the night at Arnott's house. This journey took eight days, but the gale caused considerable delay, of course.

Two days after his arrival, Mackenzie presented himself as a candidate for membership of the Royal College of Surgeons. He was examined by Sir David Dundas who, on reading a testimonial which Beer had given him, questioned him on diseases of the eye. Sir David was impressed by Mackenzie's description of the anatomy of the eye, the operations for cataract extraction and its removal by keratonyxis and finally encouraged him to settle as an oculist. Needless to say, he passed the examination.

On 5th May, he delivered an introductory letter from Harry Rainy to Sir William Adams. The latter was one of the best-known oculists in London and had a meteoric rise to fame. He was, at this time, advertising for an assistant, not for the first time, since Rainy had also been offered a similar post, but had refused it. Sir William was apparently not liked by his colleagues. Fame had come to him as a result of his work in treating service-men who had returned from the Napoleonic Wars. He was appointed to the Greenwich Hospital for Pensioners and revolutionised the treatment of ophthalmic cases, claiming, for example, twenty-nine successes out of thirty-one cases operated upon for cataract. One eye was lost, but the other 'Failure' was discharged for habitual drunkenness! This was a very high success rate for those days. He was later given a wing of York Hospital, Chelsea, was knighted and awarded £4000 by Parliament. He was appointed oculist to the Prince Regent and the Dukes of Sussex and Kent and continued to be oculist to George IV when he ascended the throne. When he interviewed Mackenzie, he was a man of fifty-nine, but Mackenzie recorded that he struck him as being very like a 'Butler or a stammering stupid Tailor'. He later breakfasted with Adams, but Mackenzie was very much on his guard following Rainy's experience. He was offered £100 per annum and, when he consulted Arnott, the latter advised him to accept. Unconvinced, however, he wrote to Rainy, as he so often did, and the latter replied in his usual thoughtful way. 'I know no person that would be so serviceable to him in this view as yourself. I do not say this to flatter you, because I think in case you come to an agreement with Adams, the services you can render him ought unquestionably to have an influence in fixing the salary he will allow you. I think Adams has a good deal of cleverness united to a most unwearied perseverance, the most insatiable ambition. His great defect is his want of a liberal education, I am convinced he feels this, and wishes to make amends for it by availing himself of the acquirement of another'. He went on to say that £150 was little enough and £200 by no means unreasonable. He wrote, 'My objection to him is his quackery, but his being a quack does not necessarily make you one. I fancy, however, you would feel rather disagreeably situated, associated with a man who pushes himself forward at all hazards, without modesty or discretion.' However, he confessed that he thought that he had, on the whole, a warm-hearted disposition to those in whom he took an interest. This letter speaks volumes and described very accurately the objections to Sir William Adams. He was not easily put off, however, and suggested to Mackenzie that he would need to make up his mind quickly as Mannoir of Geneva would like the position. He allowed him to study the books and it became evident that the income had increased from £2000 to nearly £5,000 per annum in six years. However, like Rainy before him, Mackenzie turned it down.

Meantime, he had moved into a house at 16 Newman Street, off Oxford Street. He rented three unfurnished rooms from a Mr Davidson, a coal merchant, at £45 per annum and proudly ordered a brass plate for the door. Thus began his attempt to establish himself as a general practitioner in London, but he still wanted very much to lecture on Anatomy or to be an ophthalmologist. He looked around again for a theatre in which to lecture and advertised for one in *The Times*. Arnott told him that a Mr Brodie would let him have his, but he changed his mind. He evidently found somewhere suitable for on 1st June he gave an advertisement to the *Morning Post* for a course of Lectures on Diseases of the Eye. Unfortunately, only two people came to his introductory lecture, his friend Arnott and a Dr Chub. The following week, only three people attended. He persevered, however, and completed the course five weeks later.

His second series began in October and five attended of whom three became pupils. On the same day he wrote in his diary, 'Not a sixpence of professional receipts during last month!' His introductory lectures, however, were published and no less a person than Mr Abernethy called upon him to congratulate him and to predict success.

Meantime, James Armour had been appointed to the recently opened Glasgow Fever Hospital in September 1818, at a salary of £54 per annum. Armour at this time was far from pleased with Mackenzie and, in October of that year, on receipt of a copy of some essays which the latter had sent him, wrote scolding him for not writing longer letters and then criticising, very severely, the essays! 'You write me half-a-dozen lines and call it a letter and, having written me two or three such scraps, you immediately exclaim I am sadly in your debt. But to be sure you are a Lecturer, an Oculist and a great man and in London and therefore cannot afford time to be particular to your friends who are no lecturers and no great men and who live not in the Capital – nor with men of talents – you are dreadfully short in your letters, general in your narrations and close about your affairs. However, as you are about to illuminate the world as an author and are busy in acquiring yourself a name and a place in the temple of fame and are labouring hard to raise yourself a monument more lasting than brass! I suppose I must even be content with such scanty communications and treasure them up like the oracles of the ancients . . .'.

'You should change the name . . . the very name would prevent me from buying them or even almost from reading them. I would say here is the work of some pedant who wishes to impose upon me by a long-sounding Greek-looking name, who disguises his own mother-tongue as if he were ashamed of it. . . . I think you are on the high road to quackery. The fifth page of your essays sounds very like it. Will "Essays on the Eye and its Diseases" not suffice?' 'Is there not something very bold, I had almost said presumptious, in one who was the other day a student, writing for the public, finding fault with and instructing men of experience and who have grown old in their profession?' He advises him to keep the essays for a few years. 'Recollect the works of a young professed Oculist will meet with no mercy from those who are farther advanced in the profession. Rainy is reading them. Take a good deal of his advice. I know no one more capable of giving a good one. I know no one who is a better man.' Poor James Armour. It sounds as if he rather envied Mackenzie and he was very sensitive and self-deprecatory. When he read a later essay of Mackenzie's, he found references in the introduction to people who lacked anatomical knowledge and, for some extraordinary reason, assumed that this referred to him. He complained too that Mackenzie had sent the essays without a covering letter, but Mackenzie does not seem to have liked writing letters of any kind.

As far back as June 1816, Armour had seen an advertisement for an assistant to a London surgeon. Thinking that this was probably Wardrop he applied, but received a letter from Sir William Adams, but stating no real terms. Armour thereupon declined to go for an interview saying that he detested quackery and that Adams would probably dislike him at once if he saw him. His old friend, James Sym, who took an interest in Armour, wrote to Mackenzie at this time telling him that Armour had gone into practice as soon as he had left Glasgow Royal Infirmay and that there was a strong likelihood of him marrying the matron there. This Sym regarded as something of a tragedy for such an early marriage would, as he put it, keep him in the lower ranks of the profession. Sym infers also his letter that if such a lank, thin and pale-faced man as Armour was, could be married, there was hope for the rest of them! How different were Sym and Armour. James Armour, however, was not in a great hurry to marry, for Sym wrote again eighteen months later asking if Armour were married yet. He went on to say that he had realised that he had forgotten to ask Mackenzie about this important matter whilst riding Gustavus down the

Cowcaddens. (He lived then in Kilmarnock and was probably on his way home on horseback.) He then proceeded to give Mackenzie some advice. 'There is nothing like taking a wife and, if I could afford it, I would have one tomorrow. It is much more sensible fun than getting your name on the title page of a book and becoming notorious.' Mackenzie, however, did both.

Armour did marry Miss Rebecca Witherick, matron of the Glasgow Royal Infirmary, in 1819 when he was aged twenty-seven, and they had a family. Their children were, in the main, not robust and several of them died in early life. He began practice in Glasgow on his own and worked very hard at it. He was a conscientious, kindly man and not at all pushing, but like Mackenzie, he began to lecture. In 1820, he started Midwifery lectures, but his progress was slow until 1828 when he was appointed Professor in the Andersonian Institution. His other interest was Medical Jurisprudence and he lectured from 1826 in the Portland Street Medical School. He was never physically strong so that, when he contracted typhus fever at the age of thirty-nine in 1831, he rapidly succumbed to it, leaving his wife and family largely unprovided for. This was a sad tale and accounts for much of his apparent ill-temper towards his old friend, for he was a gentle soul who, like Mackenzie, began to study Divinity before going over to the Medical Faculty.

Rainy wrote to Mackenzie at the end of November to tell him of his intended marriage to Miss Gordon of Ross-shire, but the letter arrived in London the day following the event. Six months later, Mackenzie wrote to James Armour asking what the new Mrs Rainy was like to which Armour replied, 'Mrs Rainy is a very pleasant woman, apparently well-informed and worthy of Rainy's choice. She is free from affectation. She cannot be said to be beautiful, but Rainy thinks she is (I dare say).'

Mackenzie's third series of lectures was postponed on 2nd December on account of the Queen's funeral, but two days later, five people came and two became pupils. He gave five series in all between 1st July, 1818 and 10th February, 1819, and at the last, seven army surgeons attended, the largest number of all. Although Mackenzie was to gain fame as a lecturer in later years, his start in London was far from encouraging. He seems to have had plenty of friends, most of them apparently Scottish, but it must have been a worrying time for him, especially as his practice does not seem to have flourished very well. Harry Rainy is reported to have defended his friend staunchly and put his lack of success down to his inability to charge big enough fees.

Mackenzie was determined to gain as much knowledge as possible and on 26th October, 1818, he attended a meeting of the Medico-Chirurgical Society at which he was proposed for admission. His sponsors were Wardrop, Scudamore and Longstaff. 'Wee Scuddy' was proving to be a friend and not for the last time. His application was duly considered and, on 22nd December, he was duly admitted at this meeting. Wardrop read a paper on Rheumatic Ophthalmia and another member contended that these cases were not really rheumatic in origin since they were not relieved by bleeding.

The next meeting of the Medico-Chirurgical Society was in January 1819, and Mackenzie heard a paper read by Blundel on Blood Transfusion for a case of Scirrhus of the Pylorus. The patient lived for fifty or sixty hours, and was somewhat revived, after twelve ounces of blood repeated some hours later. There was also a paper on rattlesnake bite by Dr Ashburner, an acquaintance of Mackenzie who had studied in Glasgow, and there was a paper on Sulphur Baths.

Mackenzie's old friend, the Rev. Adam Boyd, who seemed to have a great interest in medicine, came to London in January and accompanied him to the next meeting of the Society. He heard about elephantiasis in Hindustan and poisoning by nux vomica. Three days later they went together to the House of Commons and heard the Corn Bill being debated. They were struck by the sharpness of Canning and the plainness of Vansittart.

On 1st February, his fourth series of lectures only attracted two people and he seems to have abandoned this one, for he started again on 10th February on what was to prove his last course. He went on attending the Medico-Chirurgical Society meetings and on 15th February, 1819, he attended the Hunterian Oration at the Royal College of Surgeons given by Abernethy, his old instructor and admirer from Barts.

Like Rainy, he was not averse to attending the theatre and one winter evening went to Drury Lane to see Kean acting in a new play of Brutus written by Howard Bayne. Mackenzie reported it very shortly as 'Above mediocrity'.

His interest in Ophthalmology, however, continued. This had been aroused whilst still a student and in 1816, he had written a paper for the Medical Society of Glasgow College entitled, 'An Outline of the Symptoms of Inflammation of the Conjunctiva and of the Cornea,' and Rainy, at his request, had sent him a list of books about Ophthalmology whilst the latter was studying in London in 1814. On 6th March, 1819, an essay on *Lachrymal Diseases*, written by Mackenzie was published, price 2/6d.

Along with Arnott and Gordon he was still busy with the *Quarterly Journal of Foreign Medicine and Surgery* which ran from 1818 until 1823 and then changed its name to *Anderson's Quarterly Medical Journal* published by another company. In the first volume it was considered that about one third came from Mackenzie's pen since there was a description of Beer's work in Vienna and a critical review of the Continental methods of extracting cataracts. He seems to have continued to contribute until 1826.

These papers and articles are proof enough of his continued interest in Ophthalmology, but in June 1819, he came to the decision to try to establish an Eye Infirmary in Southwark. This seems an incredible step for a young man of twenty-eight, a period when most ophthalmologists are trying to carve out a career for themselves without worrying about a new Infirmary. His friend Gordon seems to have had a hand in it for a letter survives from a Mr Iain Reynolds to Dr Gordon asking for the prospectus of the proposed Eye Infirmary to be in his hands by 10th instant. He was anxious to have this so that he could pass it on to Mr Complen prior to a meeting of the Merchant Taylor's Company at which he hoped to see several gentlemen of 'Considerable respectability whose interest he wished to secure for the promotion of an intended charity'.

The plan, a copy of which is still in existence, stated that it was proposed to establish in the Borough of Southwark an Infirmary for the Relief of the Poor afflicted with Diseases of the Eye. Mackenzie pointed out that there was an extensive and increasing population in this district and that great advantages had already been derived from such institutions, both in London and elsewhere. There were, in fact, two such in London already; the Eye Infirmary in Charterhouse Square, which was to become the Moorfields Eye Hospital founded in 1804 and the Royal Westminster Ophthalmic Hospital in New Oxford Street founded in 1816, but both were situated north of the Thames and Mackenzie pointed out with justification that it was very difficult for patients to find their way to Charterhouse Square (he does not mention the Royal Westminster) and the incidence of blindness and suffering would therefore be increased. The proposal concludes, 'The establishment of an Eye Infirmary warmly recommends itself, on these accounts, to the patronage of the Public. Nor can there be any more appropriate manner, both of expressing towards God, whose all-seeing intelligence penetrates the Universe, our gratitude for the blessings we enjoy, and of imitating, at a humble distance, his never-failing beneficence, than by relieving the distresses of our fellow-men, and by rendering to them such assistance as is promised by the proposed Institution.'

The practical point of how the money was to be raised was also printed. A subscriber of ten guineas was to become a life governor and an annual subscriber of one guinea was to be an annual governor. There were to be three types of patients.

(1) In-patients on whom operations were to be performed in the Infirmary.
(2) Patients who were visited at their homes and operations performed there if the Infirmary were unable to admit them as in-patients.
(3) Out-patients to whom advice and medicines were to be supplied gratis.

Each governor was to have the right to recommend two patients and a subscription of ten guineas at first, or of one guinea annually, entitled the subscribers to have one out-patient constantly under the care of the Infirmary.

Unfortunately, the whole plan fell through as Mackenzie decided to leave London two months later. It seems that he was the real instigator of the plan as nobody carried it to a conclusion. Southwark has a fine Eye Hospital now in St George's Circus, but it was in 1857 and not 1819 that the South London Ophthalmic Hospital came into being. The Royal prefix was added in 1869 when the Princess Royal agreed to be Patron and in 1890 it became known as the Royal Eye Hospital.

It may seem strange that Mackenzie decided to come home at such a juncture, but fate, in the person of Granville Pattison, took a hand. In 1818, the latter committed his greatest indiscretion. In 1816, he had been accused of unprofessional conduct by Dr Hugh Miller in the Glasgow Royal Infirmary. It seems that he did amputations on two patients, both of whom died, and Miller felt at least one of them should have been allowed to die in peace. Pattison was censured by the managers and Hugh Miller, who was a manager at the time, was asked to resign whilst retaining his wards, as it was decided that no surgeon or physician should hold both appointments. Pattison was furious and challenged Miller which, very sensibly, Miller declined. Pattison thereupon posted him as a coward in the Tontine Coffee Room.

But worse was to follow. In December 1818, a doctor's wife in Glasgow was delivered of a child which the doctor asserted was not his; Granville Pattison was the father, he said. The doctor sued his wife for divorce on the grounds of her misconduct with Pattison and won his case. When the news leaked out Pattison strenuously denied it even to the extent of protesting his innocence before his students. Nobody really believed him and he felt compelled to make his plans to go to America. He had applied for a vacant post of Professor of Anatomy before the story became known. He did well in America after further ups and downs and it seems that he learned sense ultimately.

Meantime, Harry Rainy seized the opportunity to try to persuade Mackenzie to return to Glasgow since he saw that Pattison's dissecting rooms would soon become available. As early as March 1819, he wrote to tell Mackenzie of Pattison's misdemeanour and putting the idea into his mind. The decision to return to Glasgow, however, must have been made quickly in the end as he would hardly have begun to establish a new Eye Infirmary in June if he meant to leave London shortly.

On 31st July, 1819, Rainy wrote to Mackenzie saying that there was a rumour that Turnbull, Pattison's dissector had already gone to America and that Pattison's lease was up, but the proprietors would not let the rooms until Pattison definitely relinquished them. The rent was £36 per annum. 'Nothing can be done here until you are on the spot,' he wrote. 'I think you should not lose a single day in setting off. You will have a great deal to do to prepare two sets of lectures for the winter and get arrangements made for dissecting etc. You can do no good whatever in London at present, since you have resolved to try your fortune among us. I am never for half-measures – a moment's reflection will convince you that it is utterly impossible for your friends here, in your absence, to get everything arranged for your commencing your lectures. You will find the procuring of subjects, and the preliminary arrangements for this purpose, though not mysterious, yet a pretty difficult undertaking.'

The Andersonian Institution in John Street had only one lecture room and Pattison gave popular lectures here on Anatomy and Physiology with dissections prepared at his rooms in College Street and it was these rooms that Rainy was anxious that Mackenzie should take over. He even went so far as to interview a young man who had been recommended to him as a dissector with considerable experience in resurrecting. The rooms had become known as Allan Burns' rooms as the latter had occupied them before Pattison. Burns, who was a brilliant anatomist and the younger brother of Professor John Burns, Professor of Surgery at Glasgow University, died young in 1813 and Pattison occupied them thereafter. The proprietors promised not to re-let them without giving Rainy the chance to take them over. Accordingly, he jumped at the chance and the matter was settled.

Pattison had been Professor of Anatomy in the Andersonian Institution, but of course, there could be no guarantee that Mackenzie would be appointed to this post. Rainy, however, thought that he had a good chance.

On 14th August, 1819, Mackenzie wrote in his Diary: 'Tomorrow I leave for Leith. How indifferent I feel to localities. Leave London for Glasgow as some men would one room of their house for another. Go to obtain Allan Burns' dissecting room, there to lecture on Anatomy. Dr Henry Walker stays in my rooms till I am settled. Information from Monro about resurrecting.' On 6th October of the same year he wrote, 'Elected Professor of Anatomy in Anderson's Institution.' He had been disappointed shortly before by failing to obtain a Lectureship in Anatomy in London and this appointment must have cheered him immensely.

So the die was cast, but it was as an anatomist that he returned to his native city and he was still undecided about his future. He was willing to let it look after itself and, although the period in London must have seemed very unpromising, the future was indeed rosy had he but known it.

CHAPTER 8

Back Home to Glasgow

SO WILLIAM MACKENZIE came back to Glasgow. He set sail from London on 15th August, 1818, bound for Leith. He probably chose the sea route rather than the coach roads on account of the large quantity of baggage he possessed. Coach passengers were liable to be restricted to fourteen pounds and Mackenzie was bringing back eight cases of books and specimens, one case of phials, five large trunks and some smaller items. In view of his unfortunate experience with his luggage on board the *Lady Jane James* he decided to have it shipped on board several different boats and asked Henry Walker to stay in his rooms in London and arrange it. Walker was very doubtful about this arrangement and finally wrote, rather angrily, to Mackenzie on 9th September that he had despatched his books and preparations in eight boxes by the Leith Smack, but he had done nothing about the trunks. The expense was enormous. 'So I will thank you for definite orders relative to your book-case etc., etc., in future.' 'I have acted according to instructions, but in future I mean to use my own judgment which is something better than yours.' It seems that all went well on this occasion, but Henry Walker disappears from the scene. The 71st Regiment continued to serve in the Army of Occupation in France until October 1818, but Walker may have left the Regiment by this time.

Mackenzie set up house at No. 5 North Albion Street (Ingram Street at that time divided the Albion Street of today into North and South portions). It may be that he already owned this house since it is known that he received £22 per annum whilst he was out of Glasgow for the rent of a house. At one point in 1818, Harry Rainy wrote to him to say that his income was £80 from a Mr Falconer plus the money from the rent and the balance was 1/2½d which was not a very great sum even in the nineteenth century. The house was on the west side and presumably a little south of the present *Citizen* Office. It may indeed have belonged to Mackenzie's father for there is no indication as to how long he lived in Queen Street and the description of young William walking to school across George Square may have been fanciful.

This was a turning-point in Mackenzie's life. His efforts to make a living in London must have been discouraging in the extreme and, in the light of his subsequent brilliant career, difficult to understand. It is unlikely that his Lowland Scottish speech was against him, although some Scottish lecturers were reputed to be ununderstandable to their English

E

listeners. Many Scots succeeded in making a good living in London although Scottish folk in Mackenzie's day still spoke the broad Scots dialect which is not used so much now. His diminutive stature is unlikely to have been a disadvantage and he was reputed to have been prematurely grey and lost his hair at an early age. These last two deficiencies might well have been an advantage in 1816, giving him an air of maturity and wisdom. Lack of inches was a common complaint in Glasgow even as late as the 1914–18 War and the Highland Light Infantry (The City of Glasgow Regiment) raised a Battalion of 'Bantams' who could be as little as five feet two inches tall.

Perhaps he was altogether too modest. In at least one of his obituary notices, he is described as completely free of arrogance and his loyal old friend, Harry Rainy, had put his lack of success down to his inability to charge big enough fees. At this late date, it is impossible to say exactly what was amiss. London is a big place and doctors can be lost in it if they have no contacts with local colleagues. He seems to have been friendly with James Wardrop, the Edinburgh man who was oculist and general surgeon and who was surgeon-extraordinary to the Prince Regent both before and after he became George IV. He also had contacts with Charles Scudamore, who was reputed to be moving in the best circles. Besides, many Scots had made good in London, but something went wrong.

On the credit side, however, he had succeeded in taking over the lecture-room previously occupied by Granville Pattison in College Street. This had become a well-known establishment for the up and coming extramural teachers and this was a good start. His foot was on the first rung of the ladder at last and he was about to become the Professor of Anatomy and Surgery at the Andersonian Institute. This Institute was the product of a grandiose scheme to found a University which was to have been in opposition to Glasgow University which had been founded in 1451. When John Anderson died he left a will naming thirty-six professors along with details of the four Faculties which were to be founded, Arts, Law, Divinity and Medicine. There were to be Bachelor and Master or Doctor Degrees in each. Unfortunately, the amount left was only £1000 which was quite inadequate and the only Faculty to be formed in 1796 was the Medical one. The only Professor named in the will to take up his post was John Burns, Professor of Anatomy and Surgery who lectured in private rooms in Virginia Street and then at 10 College Street. Like so many anatomists, he fell foul of the law over exhumation and was only allowed to continue lecturing on condition that he confined his activities to Surgery and Midwifery. In 1816, however, his younger brother, Allan, joined him and ran the dissecting rooms where he became a brilliant dissector and demonstrator, although no lecturer. He died prematurely in 1813 and Granville Pattison took up his post in the College Street School. In spite of Allan Burns' death, Mackenzie still referred to the premises as Allan Burns' dissecting rooms in 1819.

Mackenzie's hopes were all realised when he was appointed Professor of Anatomy and Surgery at the Andersonian Institute in succession to Granville Pattison who had left Glasgow by this time under a cloud. This was a real turning-point in Mackenzie's life and from then on, he never looked back. His lectures were an immediate success ad it is recorded that he had fifty-seven students for Anatomy and Surgery and twenty-nine for Diseases of the Eye during his first year. In addition, he gave lectures on Medical Jurisprudence, but had to call on James Armour to carry out the experiments as he had no aptitude for these. By 1823, he had eighty-two taking his lectures on the Eye and Ear. Gone were the days of lecturing to empty seats and only a few occupied by his friends, but above all, he was doing what he had wanted to do for many years and what he did with increasing fame for the rest of his long life. This ability to propagate knowledge was his outstanding characteristic and he has gone down in history as a great teacher by the spoken and written word.

A black cloud appeared to darken his sky, however, in the shape of a court action against him, presumably for body-snatching. The appointment of a young man to a Chair of Anatomy would be noted by the authorities and they would take an early opportunity of showing him where he stood. We find him writing to his friends in London to see what they could do to help. James Gordon came to his rescue by interviewing his influential friends. Sir Charles Bell was probably an old friend from Edinburgh days and his brother, George J. Bell, was an advocate in Edinburgh. The latter was the brother-in-law of John Shaw, one of the faithful Scots who attended Mackenzie's lectures in London and between them they came to Mackenzie's rescue. George Bell asked the Lord Advocate to have the case transferred to Edinburgh. There it was brought up and then postponed until it was forgotten, which is one way of dealing with an unpleasant situation, if an unorthodox one.

The dissecting rooms were sometimes referred to as 'Mr Armour's, College Street', as in the case of a letter dated 11th September, 1819, from Dr James Sym of Kilmarnock referring to what must have been almost his first eye patient. It gives an interesting account of the treatment of blepharitis in these days. Dr Sym wrote, 'The case had a course of mercury, has been bled and had the inner surface of the eye-lids rubbed with blue vitriol before he applied to me. His general health was much impaired, though there is no particular sympton which indicates Scrofula. I have paid more heed to his general health than the local disease. A course of washes, sulphuric acid, sea-bathing, nourishing diet and attention to the bowels. He had several blisters behind his ears. I kept them open as well as I could. I emptied the blood vessels of his eyes generally every day to render them better for some time. He has employed Vinum Opii, Zinc Acetate, Zinc Sulphate, Silver Nitrate and, to the right eye, a solution of Alum. None of them has agreed so well as the Vinum Opii.'

James Gordon kept in touch with him by letter from London. He was having some difficulty with the *Quarterly Journal of Foreign Medicine* too. It must have been a very difficult task in those days of slow communications. He found time to write to Mackenzie in the autumn of 1818, 'Comment Vont les Malades? My patient at Hackney is, I am sorry to say, quite well and I must take my leave of him, but he has promised to recommend me in consequence of the surprising case I have performed. Dr Solomon hear!' Mackenzie was not the only young doctor who was having a thin time. A year later he showed great interest in his friend's behaviour and wrote, 'I am glad to hear from Boyd that you go regularly to Church. It will conduce as much to your respectability as comfort and happiness. I hope you will not adopt the Chalmerian style in your lectures! The number of young men in our profession destitute of employment is beyond calculation.'

One of the few references to his family affairs is contained in a letter from a Mr Donald Ross of 36 High Street, in the spring of 1818, whilst Mackenzie was still in London. This referred to the will of the late Andrew Mackenzie which had been deposited with William's late father, James Mackenzie. Donald Ross had married the daughter of Andrew who was probably William Mackenzie's uncle and it was requested that the will be handed over to Mr and Mrs Ross so that they could adjust matters between themselves. It is a little suggestive of some family squabble between husband and wife, but the outcome will never be known.

Mackenzie's international reputation may be said to have begun in 1819, when a Mr James Campbell wrote from Orangehill, Tobago, asking Mackenzie to send him a pair of spectacles as he could not see clearly more than twenty yards. The ordering of spectacles in 1819 was not a very precise art, but it was not quite so haphazard as this. Shortly after his return to Glasgow, Mackenzie made two important arrangements. He became a Member of the Faculty of Physicians and Surgeons as opposed to being a Licentiate. He considered that this step was desirable if he was going to set up as a specialist in Glasgow. His friend, Armour, thought that it was hard that a Member of the Royal College of Surgeons of England should be asked to pay the full fee of £150, especially as it was only £100 when Mackenzie took the Licence in 1815, but was raised in the interval.

The second action was to join the Glasgow Medical Society. The records show that he joined in January 1819, but by then he had not yet returned to Glasgow and it is unlikely that he would trouble to join the Society when he was unlikely to be able to attend meetings. It seems that the proper date was 1820 and the scribe forgot that the date had changed on 1st January. Surprisingly, he does not seem to have been at first a very enthusiastic member. The rules of the Society were strict. Each member had to read a paper on request on pain of a fine and a member must accept office or similarly pay up. At the first meeting of the winter session in 1820, Mackenzie requested leave of absence for the whole session which was granted. In fact, he did not deliver a lecture for over two years and then his subject was 'Remarks Contributive to the Natural History of

Puro-Mucous Inflammation of the Conjunctiva'. However, he regularly failed to deliver his lectures and the secretary was finally asked to write to him informing that his non-attendance would be excused provided he was actually engaged in the delivery of his lectures during the hour of the Society's meetings. He seems to have reformed, for he did not resign until 1836, by which time, he had been a vice-president for a year. By this time, Mackenzie was becoming famous and increasingly busy and may not have found time to devote to the Society.

It has been generally supposed that Mackenzie married late in life which is quite correct, but there is recorded in the Parochial Register of Glasgow, the marriage of 'William Mackenzie, Surgeon in Glasgow and Isabella Hay residing in Barony Parish, married 18th November, 1823, by Mr Benjamin Mardon, Unitarian Minister in Glasgow'. She was the daughter of the late Mr James Hay, farmer in Elgin. A daughter was born to the Mackenzies on 13th April, 1825, but it seems clear that Mrs Mackenzie died young as her name does not appear in the Mackenzie household in the first census dated 1841 and William Mackenzie is described as a widower in the 1851 census. The exact date of her death is unknown. In fact, Mackenzie leaves us very few clues as to his personal affairs altogether.

In these days Mackenzie was giving serious thought to establishing an Eye Infirmary in Glasgow similar to the one which he unsuccessfully mooted for Southwark. This was the time when special hospitals were springing up all over the country. The first in England would appear to have been the St John's Hospital for Diseases of the Eyes, Legs and Breasts opened in 1771 in Holborn by William Rowley. Its extraordinary title suggests that the hospital was founded by an unusual type of man. He had the reputation of being a great self-advertiser and a plagiarist. Not surprisingly, it only lasted for two or three years. Another, the Royal Infirmary for Diseases of the Eye was founded by Sir Wathen Waller in 1804. This one survived until 1871.

In 1804, however, Moorfields Eye Hospital was founded by C. J. Saunders and prospered. The West of England Eye Infirmary at Exeter was founded by Sir William Adams in 1808 and the Bristol Eye Hospital in 1810, the Manchester Royal Eye Hospital in 1815, the Liverpool Eye and Ear Infirmary in 1820 and the Birmingham and Midland Eye Hospital in 1823. An early Eye Infirmary in Edinburgh became defunct, but there were plenty of examples of special hospitals for Diseases of the Eye flourishing when Mackenzie came back to Glasgow in 1819.

Special hospitals and indeed specialisation itself were not very popular at this time and there was considerable opposition from the medical profession. They took exception to the fact that the special hospital treated only one part of the anatomy and did not regard the eye in relation to the whole body. Special hospitals were even described as a 'monstrous evil'. When Sir William Adams established the West of England Eye Infirmary in Exeter in 1808, he did so against the opposition of the local medical practitioners who did not approve of specialisation at all. Evidently, it was assumed that a medical practitioner, having qualified in Medicine, should be capable of dealing with any abnormality in any part of the body. Attempts were made, however, to make exception of Eye Hospitals, but without much success. These had come into being largely as a result of the Napoleonic Wars. When Napoleon invaded Egypt, a British Expeditionary Force was sent to prevent him from cutting our supply-route to India. This operated from 1800 to 1802 and many British soldiers contracted trachoma. Some spoke of whole companies being blinded by the disease. Public conscience was stirred and the result was the founding of Moorfields Eye Hospital in 1804 which, in spite of the early criticisms and fortunately for posterity, survived. Many other Eye Hospitals, however, closed down after varying periods.

Mackenzie felt the need of such a special infirmary in Glasgow and called on George Cunningham Monteath for assistance. They were already well acquainted and Monteath was well known as Glasgow's premier eye specialist. He was also well connected. His uncle was Dr James Monteath who practised in Stockwell Street and his father was the Rev. James Monteath, D.D., Minister of Houston. One of his brothers was also a medical practitioner and another was a lawyer. He appears to have been connected with the Monteath family who were manufacturers in Anderston.

The local medical practitioners and some influential Glasgow gentlemen were called to a meeting in the old Town House at Glasgow Cross by the Lord Provost on 10th February, 1824. There they met Mackenzie and Monteath and the two young ophthalmologists (Monteath was only thirty-five) stressed to the meeting that patients suffering from eye diseases were not availing themselves of the services of the Royal Infirmary and very few had been admitted there. They very rightly pointed out that blindness might ensue if some cases were not properly treated. The gentlemen present had doubtless already made up their minds that an Eye Infirmary was essential, but it was necessary to make a formal decision and Henry Monteath, Esq., M.P., proposed and James Ewing, Esq., seconded that 'This meeting do highly approve of the establishment of an Infirmary in Glasgow for the Relief of the Poor Afflicted with Diseases of the Eye'. The first president was Henry Monteath and twelve directors were appointed, including the Lord Provost. Mr John Alston became the first treasurer. The two surgeons were, of course, William Mackenzie and George Monteath.

This expeditious founding of an Eye Infirmary was in marked contrast to William Mackenzie's inability to found a similar establishment in Southwark, but it must be remembered that Mackenzie was only twenty-eight in 1819 and was still unknown in a strange city. In 1824 he had become known as an able lecturer in the Anderson College of Medicine and was back in his own native city. Perhaps, even more important, he had the support of his friend, George Monteath who belonged to a well-known Glasgow family. It was Henry Monteath, M.P., who proposed that the Eye Infirmary should be established and the first secretary was James Monteath, George's brother, of the legal firm of Black, Honeyman & Monteath which firm provided the secretaries for the Infirmary for the first one hundred and twenty-one years of its existence. James Ewing who seconded the motion lived in the Crawford Mansion at the top of Queen Street which he had purchased about 1815. He sold it in 1838 for the building of Queen Street Station at presumably a large profit. On account of the rookery in his estate, he was nicknamed 'Craw' Ewing and one of the hotels on the west side of George Square was named the 'Crow Hotel' for the same reason. He was a good friend of the Eye Infirmary and was one of its first directors.

The Eye Infirmary began in a small house at No. 19 Inkle Factory Lane. This was a narrow lane which ran from North Albion Street, past the end of the Old Shuttle Street Church on the right and the 'Penny School' on the left into Shuttle Street itself. The Inkle (or tape) Factory was probably one in Ingram Street beside the St David's-Ramshorn Church. If so, the lane must have meandered considerably. The late Dr Leslie Buchanan thought that the Infirmary building was probably at the corner of North Albion Street and the Lane.

The Infirmary had no beds at first and any operations that were performed took place in the patients' homes, probably on the kitchen table to be exact. Two beds, however, were supplied in 1825 and the Infirmary gradually developed.

Whilst William Mackenzie is regarded as the founder of the Glasgow Eye Infirmary, one cannot escape regarding George Cunningham Monteath as the engineer. Unfortunately, he only survived the foundation of the Infirmary for four years for on 25th January, 1828, he succumbed to an attack of 'Fever' contracted on a night journey. He was Glasgow's first oculist and a very able one. He translated a text book on Diseases of the Eye written by Weller of Berlin and added some of his own material in 1821. It is in two volumes and contains some early coloured pictures of diseases of the eye which are noted for their clarity. If Monteath had survived, ophthalmology might have progressed more rapidly in Glasgow, but Mackenzie seems to have been the driving force and those were the days of the great individualists in medicine. They could, however, have formed a formidable team with Monteath's ability and valuable connections and Mackenzie's clear, enquiring mind which thought out problems and tried to find solutions time and time again until he made order out of chaos.

So fame came to Mackenzie with the founding of the Glasgow Eye Infirmary and his practice prospered. He moved to a house at 46 Wilson Street about 1824 and in 1826 to Spreull's Court, which is still there at 182 Trongate, almost opposite Turner's Court, where Harry Rainy lived. It was whilst they were living at Spreull's Court that the Mackenzies' only child, Isabella, died on 21st March, 1828, at the age of two years eleven months. By 1830, he was ensconced in George Square at No. 68. George

Square had developed considerably since his boyhood. No. 68 was on the north side between North Hanover Street and North Frederick Street and this side was considered the most elegant side. It is still largely unchanged. The central area of the Square by 1830 was laid out in gardens with proper railings round them, but a sketch drawn in 1825 showed the solitary statue of Sir John Moore at the southern edge of the very untidy-looking central plot. Pigs are seen feeding on it and housewives are shown washing blankets by the well-established practice of trampling them in tubs. The paling is of wood and tumbledown. Small boys are trying to pull down Sir John's statue.

During Mackenzie's stay in George Square, the statues of Sir Walter Scott and of James Watt were erected and it became a very desirable part of Glasgow in which to reside. George Monteath had resided at No. 15 which was probably on the east side of the Square where the City Chambers are situated now. It was a pleasant, genteel part of Glasgow and it came in for some criticism indirectly in 1834 in the *Reformer's Gazette*, an early publication in favour of the beginnings of the Labour movement. It appears that two young men, William S. Bentley and Thomas Hussey were charged with being drunk and disorderly on a Sunday evening and Communion Sunday at that. Bentley lived at 70 George Square and pledged his watch as a fine whilst Hussey paid two guineas. The writer in the Gazette was very indignant at this and pointed out that if the young offenders had not been gentlefolk, they would have been sent to prison. The event seems to have impressed Mackenzie because a copy of the *Reformer's Gazette* is preserved amongst his papers. It is dated 24th April, 1834 and was priced at twopence.

About a quarter of a mile away lived Dr and Mrs Harry Rainy in Montrose Street. They were married in 1819 and were bringing up their family at this time. Mrs Rainy's father was Captain Gordon of Invercarron of the 73rd Highlanders. This, surprisingly perhaps, was the regiment in which the young Arthur Wellesley was first commissioned in 1787. It was a new regiment at that time and this might explain why the Irish-born youth of seventeen made his way to Scotland. Perhaps young Mrs Rainy boasted to her friends in her nice parlour in Montrose Street that her father had taught the future Duke of Wellington a thing or two about soldiering. Who knows?

North Albion Street played quite a large part in the making of Glasgow's history. Apart from housing William Mackenzie and the Glasgow Eye Infirmary, it contained the first Congregational Church in Glasgow. Just North of Inkle Factory Lane was the Greyfriars Church. This was a Secession Church, the successor to the old Shuttle Street Church at the other end of the Lane. It was also called Dr Dick's Chapel locally. A little further south was an early Mechanics Institute. These old edifices have all gone now and the most imposing building now is the *Citizen* newspaper office.

CHAPTER 9

The Author

THE YOUNG medical practitioner, then of the nineteenth century was very much dependent on lectures for his education. This can be seen by the number of extramural medical schools in Glasgow. There were three in the area east of George Square, the Andersonian Institute in John Street, the Portland Street School and the College Street School. The Andersonian Institute was too small to house all it was meant to do and the College Street School provided the accommodation. There was considerable competition for these lectureships and William Mackenzie, as we have already seen, was prominent as a teacher.

By 1830, Mackenzie had proved himself an able writer as well as a lecturer. Whilst still in London, he wrote a modest essay on the *Diseases of the Lacrymal Organs*, published at 2/6d, and another in 1823 on *A Description of the Human Muscles*; to which is added *a table of their combined actions*. This was also priced at 2/6d and both could be obtained at the College Street rooms. Also available was *A magnified View of the Ear* which could be bought for 1/-.

Amongst Mackenzie's letters there is a curious little note from an unknown friend which states, 'Should I not have arrived before Dr G. C. M. sends for. . . . you will find the aforesaid under Harry's bed.' G. C. M., would be Dr George Cunningham Monteath and Harry would be Harry Rainy. It is addressed to Mackenzie at the Royal Infirmary. What the mysterious object under the bed was, we shall never know, but it may well have been some part of the human body illicitly taken by one of the doctors for further study or dissection.

In 1824, Mackenzie wrote a splendid pamphlet on the problem of the supply of bodies for dissection in the Anatomy Rooms. At this time, the only bodies available for this purpose were those of executed criminals, a limited source, and those of public-spirited individuals who left their bodies voluntarily in their wills, an even scantier source. It was quite obvious that this was entirely inadequate and the medical profession set out to provide itself with bodies by illegal means. Medical students and professional 'Resurrectionists' were employed to dig up the recently buried and earned the praise of the anatomists and the condemnation of the forces of law and order and of the populace in general. William Mackenzie felt very strongly on the subject and directed his not inconsiderable talent for writing towards a more rational approach to the problem. In 1824, he wrote a powerful appeal in the form of a pamphlet entitled, *An appeal to the Public and to the Legislature on the necessity of affording Dead Bodies to the Schools of Anatomy by Legislative Enactment.*

The pamphlet runs to thirty-six pages and, characteristically, not only did Mackenzie point out the deficiencies of the system, but he also gave extensive directions on how it was to be put right. The Medical profession was well acquainted with the situation. Accordingly, he addresses himself to the lay-public in general and the legal profession in particular. Skillfully, he points out that the practice of Medicine had two great objects, apart from the curing of diseases, namely the preservation of health and the solution of many important questions in connection with the administration of justice. As examples, he quotes the collaboration with the legislator on questions of public health, prisons and the Armed Forces and also in cases of court proceedings arising from charges of rape, murder, adultery etc. In order, therefore, to be of assistance to the legal profession, the medical practitioner must have a first-class basic knowledge of medicine of which the very heart is the study of Anatomy. This, he points out under the present system is impossible of attainment owing to the shortage of bodies for dissection. A knowledge of Anatomy, he points out, would enable many lives to be saved on the field of battle since three-quarters of those who died in battle did so from loss of blood, a reminder of the primitive state of the Army medical services in those days. He points out, with justice, how wrong it would be to expect a surgeon to operate on a living person without a thorough knowledge of the structures which he is to divide and to repair. He goes on to point out that it is only by seeing the tissues on the dead body and not only seeing them, but by touching them that he can gain the necessary knowledge. Furthermore, he states that it is essential for the student, not only to see a dissection being done, but he must do it himself. 'A Carpenter' he points out, 'would not be a good craftsman by lectures only.' It is a humbling thought that Mackenzie wrote that it was the lot of comparatively few of those who later became surgeons to repeat even once the chief operations on the body. These were in 1824, of course, few in number, but one can imagine the tragedies which might occur when the operations had to be done so quickly by reason of the absence of anaesthetics.

If no adequate supplies of cadavers were to be made available, Mackenzie suggests that the only alternative source of training would be one which he shuddered even to mention, namely practising on the bodies of the poor. The rich, he stated, would always be able to consult those with experience, but the poor would have no choice. This proposal he rejects out of hand. It is worth quoting the crescendo to which Mackenzie mounts in his indignation at the state of affairs then existing. It is pedantic to our eyes, but it is written in very fine prose and he certainly makes his point. 'But upon whose head, let me ask, is the guilt of this horrid sacrifice of ignorance? The surgeon is but the officiator. The worshippers of ignorance, who surround him; and who force him on, and those who have impeded and who would yet more impede, the study of Anatomy and those who, in order to give an idle protection to the dead, would not hesitate to render the healing art little better than a cruel mockery of the distressed. If it be true, that he who wilfully impedes assistance to the wretch who is expiring from a draught of poison, is equally guilty with him who mingled it, and with him who gave it, then he who by the least unnecessary word, opposes the study of Anatomy, is neither more nor less a murderer. By his opposition, he, as it were, poisons the balm of medicine, which promised to give a little ease of horrid suffering – he puts out his foot to make the Surgeon stumble, who is running with help to the wounded and the dying.'

'Would to God that the eyes of the public were open to the consequences of their idolatory of the dead! They would then spurn with contempt, the plans of those ignorant men who have vapoured over their midnight bowls, that they would put an end to Anatomy, blind to the widely disastrous effects, which their plans, if carried on, must speedily produce on the best and dearest interests of humanity. Instead of seeking to degrade the Anatomist or to disturb him in his pursuits, the public, if they rightly understood the matter, and could for a moment listen to reason, not to passion, would be eager to honour and assist a man, who for the sake of relieving the sufferings of his fellow-creatures, can take up his abode with death and corruption, make the most loathsome objects on which the eye can ever look his familiar associates and even risk his life in acquiring that knowledge which is to enable him to preserve and restore the health of those who hate and persecute him.'

Characteristically, Mackenzie weighs up the objections to exhumation as well as protesting that it is the only alternative. He stresses the distress it gives to the relations of the deceased, the violation to property in disturbing the grave, the possibility of riots following exhumation by the public, the expense to relations of guarding the grave against the resurrectionists and the danger to students whilst carrying out their digging and later in dissecting bodies which were decomposing. With great thoroughness he then proceeds to work out how many bodies would be required and the figures are interesting. In three years, two students would need nine bodies for dissection and a tenth for operative surgery. He estimates that London would require six hundred bodies per year, Edinburgh two hundred, Dublin two hundred and Glasgow one hundred. The total needed for the Empire would be one thousand, three hundred and fifty for dissection and three hundred for operative surgery for the students and another three hundred for the demonstrations, making a total of one thousand, nine hundred and fifty. Only three hundred were available annually. As a source of these bodies, he suggests hospitals, workhouses, poorhouses, foundling houses, houses of correction and prisons. He points out that these sources must be legalised and that other countries have already done so. If not, he wrote that Anatomy would cease in this country, but with national pride, he points out that, in spite of the restrictions in this country, we still produced the Monroes, the Hunters, Baillie, Abernethy, Cooper, Bell and Barclay.

He then, again characteristically, went on to produce his plan for legislation which was as follows, in summary:

(1) A clause whereby the examination of a dead body is made part of the punishment for murder should be repealed.

(2) Exhumation should be punishable as a felony.

(3) No Diploma in Medicine or Surgery to be granted to anybody, except to those who shall produce evidence of having carefully dissected at least five human bodies.

(4) In each of the hospitals, infirmaries etc., and prisons in London, Edinburgh, Glasgow and Dublin, and, if need be, of all other towns in Great Britain and Ireland, an apartment should be appointed for the reception of the bodies of all persons dying in the said hospitals, etc., and prisons unclaimable by immediate relatives, or whose relatives decline to defray the expense of interment, which expenses shall be estimated at the rate of twenty shillings.

(5) No dead body shall be delivered from any hospital, prison or morthouse except upon the requisition of a member of the Royal College of Physicians or of Surgeons of London, Edinburgh or Dublin or of the Faculty of Physicians and Surgeons of Glasgow and upon the payment of twenty shillings into the hands of the treasurer of the hospital or prison.

(6) After twenty-eight days, an officer appointed for the purpose shall cause the remains to be placed in a coffin and decently interred.

In fairness, he quoted various objections to the above plan. It had been suggested that the hospitals would be emptied since patients would not come in if they thought that they might finish up in the dissecting room, but Mackenzie pointed out that the only people likely to be influenced by these considerations would be those who could afford private treatment and the hospital doors would be open wider for the poorer patients. He goes on to describe how he would like to take those who object to the dissecting room, which they loathe so much, to the battlefield where thousands of living men armed with every instrument of cruel death become corpses, but the public forgets the lamentations of the widow, the mother and the sister in the jubilations of victory.

He also points out that the dedication of only a very few unclaimed bodies to the humane purposes of anatomical instruction makes the public put on the mask of tender-heartedness and horror and threatens to punish the poor foolish anatomist who is cursed with an enthusiasm for the relief of suffering and foresees in the researches which he is forbidden to institute the discovery of a new or better means of curing some mortal disease. 'If,' he goes on, 'the end of war which is the defence of our country, is sufficient to justify the adoption of a means so terrible as the destruction of so many lives, surely the end of anatomical study, which is the assuagement of human suffering, is ten times sufficient to justify the dissection of the dead.' He continues by pointing out that it is possible that a patient can be permanently invalided by the work of a surgeon and is the victim, not so much of the surgeon's ignorance, as of an idolatrous respect for the dead which banned that surgeon from acquiring a knowledge of his profession.

He concludes this apologia with the words, 'Any delay in making the supply of the Schools of Anatomy a matter of legislative enactment, would be a vital injury to the best interests of this country, and of mankind at large.' These were strong words and Mackenzie obviously felt very strongly on the subject. The pamphlet extended to thirty-six pages and was in very pedantic English as was the custom of the age. It attracted a considerable amount of attention at the time, but as so often happens, it took a tragedy to force public opinion to press for a change in the law in the shape of the murders perpetrated by Burke and Hare in Edinburgh during 1828. The murderers were Irishmen who saw a good market for dead bodies (Crouch in London was paid four guineas for each) and devised a series of murders to supply the need. The Edinburgh folk finally rose in anger when it was discovered that a popular dim-witted boy called 'Daft Jamie' had disappeared and Burke and Hare were caught with a dead body, the victim of murder, in their room. It was obvious that something had to be done. Burke was hanged and Hare released since the latter had turned King's evidence on the former and, unfortunately the worthy surgeon who had received one or more bodies, Robert Knox, was compromised. Although the court which sentenced Burke to death exonerated him and his assistants from any guilt, Knox had to leave Edinburgh. He found refuge in the Portland Street Medical School for less than a month in 1844, and would become acquainted with Mackenzie who had already been in trouble with the law as we have seen. As we shall see, one of Knox's assistants, Thomas Wharton Jones, who also left Edinburgh, was already associated with Mackenzie in the writing of his *magnum opus*.

In 1829, an Act was passed making it legal to grant a licence to any graduate or licence-holder in Medicine or of a College of Physicians or Surgeons to perform dissections. It is said that the Duke of Sussex, one of George III's sons, thereupon offered his body for dissection at his death. It is doubtful if his offer was accepted. In 1832, however, Warburton's Anatomy Act was passed which is still largely the law of the land and it is worthy of note that its content is largely that suggested by William Mackenzie in his pamphlet of 1824.

Mackenzie's next publication was a booklet on treatment which he called *Outline of Therapeiology or the Science of Remedies. For the Use of Students, 1826*. Inside, there is the statement that 'Mr Mackenzie Lectures on Dietetics, Materia Medica and Pharmacy. Commence annually in November; on the Structure, Functions and Diseases of the Eye, in May;

and on Anatomy and Physiology in August. Spreull's Court, 182 Trongate, 26th October, 1826.'

The booklet consists of nineteen small pages. He explains in a foreword that Therapeiology comes from the Greek and means'A discourse on remedies' and in this booklet 'Remedies are classified, their properties explained and an enquiry instituted to what diseases each class is adapted'. He explains that 'In Therapeutics, diseases are classified, their symptoms enumerated and an enquiry instituted by what kinds of remedies they can be relieved'. It seems a subtle distinction. The remedies are tabulated and include such treatment as sleep, diet, state of mind, bathing and exercise. These are followed by pharmaceutic means such as vascular excitants (such as beer and wine), nervous excitants (such as tea, coffee and bitumen), analeptics and antiparalytics; narcotics such as opium; sedatives such as castoreum and assafetida; tonics such as gentian, quassia; astringents such as catechu and bistorta; alteratives such as hydrag and arsenic; emetics such as ipecacuanha and aqua tepida; hydragogues such as Pil. hydrag; escharotics such as the actual cautery and argent nitras; antiseptics such as acid citric, cinchona and sisymbrium nasturtium; diluents such as infus theae; demulcents such as gum arabic and prunus domesticus, mineral waters such as those from Seltzer, Carlsbad, Tunbridge, Harrogate, Moffat, Cheltenham and Pitcaithly, etc., etc.

The whole of Surgery occupies one page only and includes leeches, cupping and blood-letting. He also mentions transfusions and injection into canals and cavities, such as air into the lungs and water into the stomach. This is a very comprehensive little booklet and tends to stress the sparcity of methods of treatment in 1826. It will be noted that there is a very long list of internal medicines, but not very much surgery. This is hardly surprising when one considers that anaesthetics were not available and operations so often ended fatally. The long list of remedies must have been daunting to young students in 1826 just as it would be today. Many of the classes of drugs are no longer used, or at any rate thus described, and 'Infusum Theae' seems a pedantic way of saying 'A Pot of Tea'. There never has been a short cut to learning about drugs and there probably never will be, but it seems that it has always been difficult to present Pharmacology in an attractive and exciting form.

The next pamphlet was published in 1828 and was entitled *Outlines of a Course of Lectures on the Structure, Function and Diseases of the Eye*. In the preface, he explains that the text was based on a series of lectures which he first delivered in London in the summer of 1818 and were, so far as he believed, the earliest separate and systematic course of lectures on the eye and its diseases delivered in this country. Mackenzie deemed Professor Beer of Vienna the most distinguished oculist who had ever appeared and, having found no lectures available in London when he returned from Austria in 1818, decided to give talks on his experiences on the Continent and especially in Germany which he thought had many excellent ophthalmologists. The pamphlet was, in fact, a curtain-raiser for his great work, *A Practical Treatise on the Diseases of the Eye*, as well as an attempt to help his students in their work. It was an attempt to put in order the material for the Treatise, prior to its publication.

In the introduction, he gives a short, but masterly resumé of the reasons for the study of the eye and its diseases being a separate entity. These are:

(1) The organ of vision is the most complicated organ of the body.
(2) Its structures and functions are peculiar and consequently the diseases are different in many respects from the diseases of other parts.
(3) The surgical operations performed on this organ are necessarily accommodated in minuteness and delicacy to the parts concerned.
(4) The diseases of the eye although in many cases purely local, frequently arise from constitutional affections, or sympathetically from diseases of remote organs.

This pamphlet ran to three editions, the last one being in 1856 when he enlarges on the four points in the introduction which now runs to thirteen pages. He points out that the eye is a very special organ since it has to be transparent in order to function properly and also because one can actually see the various structure of the eye. He also makes the point that iritis, or inflammation of the iris gives rise to symptoms which are so peculiar that they are unlike inflammation in any other part of the body.

The general practitioners of the day came in for some criticism since he accuses them for making a merit of not studying the eye particularly and 'They would have it that all the ophthalmologist's distinction of eye diseases and all his rules for operating on the eye were merely much ado about nothing and, while they persisted in unjustifiable ignorance on the subject, made awkward and mischievous attempts to perform operations they had never learned'. Whilst few general practitioners nowadays operate on eyes, there is still a steady flow of patients into the Eye Infirmary whom the general practitioner feels unwilling to treat himself. This is due, however, rather to the vastly more complicated forms of treatment now available and the general practitioner is no longer critical of the ophthalmologist on the grounds of 'Much ado about Nothing'.

There is a section on 'Ophthalmia' and in this he distinguishes between the various types of inflammation. This marks the beginnings of a more scientific approach to the diagnosis of the inflammatory diseases of the eye which had begun at the beginning of the century. Some of the conditions make strange reading, e.g. conjunctivitis, scrofulosa, porriginosa and erisypelosa; catarrho rheumatic ophthalmia; corneitis; aquo-capsulitis; antero- or postero-chrystalline-capsulitis; and chrystallinitis.

There is a long list of causes of amaurosis divided into various species. There is quoted, for example, amaurosis from plethora as an example of a loss of sentient power of the eye. There is amaurosis from absorption of the pigmentum nigrum and from narcotics, from acute eruptions, from repercussions of catarrh, from gout, from rage and from suppression of the milk.

In 1828, of course, there was no ophthalmoscope and the above list was somewhat conjectural. The ophthalmoscope was new in 1856 when the third edition came out and Mackenzie was able to enlarge on his original introduction and talk of the parts of the eye being visible. In 1828, Mackenzie was appointed Waltonian Lecturer in Ophthalmology in the University of Glasgow and this pamphlet would be for student benefit as well as forming the basis of his *magnum opus*.

Mackenzie gave the opinion that ninety cases out of one hundred inflammatory diseases in children were scrofulous and that iritis was perhaps most frequently syphilitic. Amaurosis, or blindness, frequently took origin from a distance, e.g. the digestive system, liver, kidney or uterus, he stated, and again became critical of general practitioners who diagnosed amaurosis and left it at that. Even some oculists diagnosed it and did not attempt to discriminate its varieties. Unfortunately, in those days most cases were incurable, but those that were had to be studied carefully at length. The General Hospital was not the place for this as there was little time for the study of Ophthalmology. Hence the establishment of special Eye Infirmaries.

In 1828, Mackenzie somehow found time to found the *Glasgow Medical Journal* and edited the first two editions himself. Whether he continued its publication at his own expense is not certain, but there was a change of ownership in 1868, the year of Mackenzie's death which suggests that he might have done so.

In the same year, on 14th July to be exact, William Mackenzie's name appeared on the front page of the *Glasgow Herald*. Surprisingly, this was at the foot of a testimonial to a certain Mr Keays who claimed to be an expert in the treatment of Stammering and one of his successes was a Mr James Smith of Berwickshire, a patient of Dr William Mackenzie.

Under the announcement of Mr Keay's prowess appeared a certificate from Mr Smith's employers to say that he was now able to follow his employment efficiently and then followed Mackenzie's rather luke-warm testimonial which finished with the words, 'Whereas formerly his expression was peculiar and unpleasing, he now looks and converses with an appearance of comparative intelligence'! This type of advertisement would not be acceptable in the twentieth century. Perhaps it would be so in 1828, but it is just possible that, in his enthusiasm, Mr Keays had it printed, including therein, Mackenzie's name and address, 'Spreull's Court', without the latter's permission.

The frontispiece of William Mackenzie's small book on the
Muscles of the Human Body. Actual size. 1823.
The inscription reads 'Death teaches us how to preserve Life'.

*Reproduced by kind permission of the Council of the Royal College of
Physicians and Surgeons of Glasgow.*

WILLIAM MACKENZIE IN OLD AGE

From this photograph it is estimated that his height was about 5 feet 3 inches.

Reproduced by kind permission of the Misses Lochhead, grand-nieces of Dr William Brown, William Mackenzie's partner.

HARRY RAINY IN OLD AGE

Depicted in academic robes and holding a wooden stethoscope.

CHAPTER 10

The Treatise and Later Works

WE HAVE SEEN that the student of Medicine in the early nineteenth century seems to have preferred to qualify by means of apprenticeship to a general practitioner. Those who did so through a University were inclined to be academic rather than practical, but Mackenzie, Harry Rainy and James Armour all did it this way, but combined it with clerkships at the Glasgow Royal Infirmary, thus making up for the lack of clinical knowledge.

It must have been difficult for the medical student to find enough reading material and this would help to decide him to serve an apprenticeship. In Ophthalmology there were a number of books available, but they seemed to deal with aspects of the subjects, very often cataract, for example, and one can picture the would-be ophthalmologist with a large number of small books and a larger number of thin pamphlets, rather like a collection of sheet-music secreted in the piano-stool.

In 1808, there had appeared the first of two essays on the *Morbid Anatomy of the Human Eye* written by James Wardrop of Edinburgh. This covered the diseases of the cornea and was extensively illustrated. The author was born in Bathgate, and was apprenticed to his uncle, Andrew Wardrop in Edinburgh and became an expert anatomist. He went to London in 1801 and later to Vienna where, like Mackenzie, he studied under Beer and so became interested in Opthalmology. He came back to Edinburgh where he wrote the first volume of his essays. This is a very rational attempt to classify the diseases of the cornea and to depart from the classification of all inflammatory diseases of the eyes as ophthalmia. In fact, the essays laid a very good foundation for the subsequent rapid increase in knowledge. One of the most interesting observations is on what he assumes is haziness of the cornea due to an increase in the quantity of the contents of the eyeball. He compares this in the living eye with what happens in the dead body when the contents of the eyeball are relatively increased by simple pressure or by injecting the ophthalmic veins with quick silver or pure water. He found that the cornea lost its natural transparency and acquired a milky colour. From this observation, he concluded that in the living eye, such a haziness of the cornea could be abolished by making an incision into the cornea and discharging the aqueous humor. He did this in some cases of generalised cloudiness of the cornea and found, to his satisfaction, that the cornea cleared. It is clear that these patients were suffering from acute closed-angle glaucoma and Wardrop

F

was laying down a principle of treatment which was to be developed and elaborated as the years went on, not least by William Mackenzie himself who was something of a pioneer in this field.

The second essay was not published until 1818 for reasons, he states in his preface, which need not concern the reader. In this essay, one observation of Wardrop's was the occurrence of iritis in the uninjured eye following a perforating wound of the fellow-eye. He also distinguished between the injection of conjunctival vessels in conjunctivitis and of the deeper ciliary vessels in iritis. Like so many of his contemporaries, however, he was puzzled by the apparent absence of muscle fibres in the iris, but points out that such have been demonstrated in larger animals.

On the subject of squint, he was on very unsure ground. He knew that occlusion of the non-squinting eye improved the visual acuity of the squinting one, but on the subject of corresponding points in the two retinae he was less well informed. He pointed out that a person can conquer double vision by perseverance and the theory of retinal correspondence therefore falls to the ground!

Detachment of the retina he describes as dropsy of the choroid, but of course, he only saw this condition in eyes which had been enucleated since there was no ophthalmoscope with which to diagnose it beforehand. Even then, retinal detachments remained incurable owing to a lack of understanding of their mechanism, for more than another century. However, the scientific age of Ophthalmology had begun and attempts were made to unravel the problems which had remained unsolved for so long. One extraordinary statement is made by Wardrop, however, in which he makes out that little advantage is probably derived from being endowed with a pair of eyes except that of diminishing the risk from injury or disease. It is strange that the author of such a forward-looking essay should dismiss such a complicated subject so lightly especially as he describes some form of decussation of the optic nerves, and must have appreciated that there was a great interdependence between the two eyes.

Wardrop had, in fact, a very distinguished career. He returned to London in 1808 and lived there until his death in 1869. He was appointed Surgeon Extraordinary to the Prince Regent when he had become a friend of Mackenzie in London and came to Edinburgh in the retinue of the same royal personage in 1823 when he had become George IV and later was appointed Surgeon in Ordinary to the King. One of his sons served in the Crimea as medical officer to the 7th Hussars, Britain was still somewhat behind the Continent in the publication of text-books about Ophthalmology, but Wardrop seems to have given a start to remedying this situation. George Monteath in 1821 published a little book in two volumes on Diseases of the Eye. This was a translation of work by Beer and Weller with some observations of his own added. Both Wardrop's and Monteath's books contained coloured illustrations of note.

Then in 1823, George James Guthrie published a book on ophthalmic operations. Guthrie was a rather romantic figure because he was primarily an army surgeon and served with distinction with Sir Arthur Wellesley in the Peninsular Campaign. In 1816, however, he founded the Royal Westminster Ophthalmic Hospital under the patronage of his old commander-in-chief, by now the Duke of Wellington. There was, however, still a great need for a large comprehensive text-book of Ophthalmology in English, authoritative in its utterances. This was known to William Mackenzie, who must have longed for something of the kind during his own early days of study. He knew himself to be a good lecturer and imparter of knowledge and set himself the task of filling the vacuum. The fruits of his labours were published in 1830 as *A Treatise on Diseases of the Eye* by Longman, Rees, Orme, Brown & Green of London. This extended to eight hundred and fifty-three pages and was a remarkable book for any man to write and the author was only thirty-nine years of age. It was an instantaneous success and became world-wide in its distribution. It is characteristically very systematically arranged, the first chapter being concerned with the orbit, the second with the lacrymal apparatus, the third with the eyebrow and eyelids and so on from front to back, as it were. The last chapter deals with amaurosis, but in the absence of the ophthalmoscope, this is inconclusive. Obstruction of the naso-lacrimal dust was treated by various probing procedures including silver styles and even catgut normally used as violin strings.

Squints were treated rationally so far as knowledge went at that time, but the cause was thought often to be abdominal irritation and the first essential was to give a purge or, if thought to be strumous, tonics were given. Occlusion of the better eye to bring up the sight of the amblyopic eye, however, was recommended and it was known that the better eye might become amplyopic in the course of the occlusion. The provision of spectacles was also recommended, convex lenses for the long-sighted and concave for the short-sighted and there is a long description of recommended exercises for alternating squints. This was put forward originally by Darwin in the *Philosophical Transactions* in 1778 (Vol. IXVIII Part 1, p. 86) and consisted of a thin brass gnomon which was put on the nose projecting about two and a half inches in front. By this means, the patient was not tempted to use the right eye for objects in his left field and vice versa.

In divergent squint, Mackenzie recommends a piece of black plaster on the top of the nose. Operative treatment is not mentioned. There is a large chapter on the subject of the Ophthalmiae which heartily endorses what Wardrop wrote about the need to differentiate between the various types which affect different layers of the eye. He gives eleven groups of inflammatory diseases of the eye which make interesting reading now.

    I. Conjunctivitis divided into Muco-Purosa sub-divided into Catarrhal. Contageous or Egyptian, Leucorrhoeal or Ophthalmia Neonatorum and Gonorrhoeal.

1. Conjunctivitis Scofulosa sub-divided into Phyctenular and Pustular.
2. Conjunctivitis Erysipelatosa.
3. Conjunctivitis Variolosa.
4. Conjunctivitis Morbillosa.
5. Conjunctivitis Scarlatinosa.

II. *Sclerotitis*. I. Rheumatic.
III. Corneitis I. Scofulosus.
IV. Iritis divided into
    1. Rheumatic.
    2. Syphilitic.
    3. Scrofulous.
    4. Arthritic.
V. Choroiditis.
VI. Retinitis.
VII. Aquo-Capsulitis.
VIII. Antero-Chrystallino-Capsulitis.
IX. Postero-Chrystallino-Capsulitis.
X. Vitreo-Capsulitis.
XI. Christallinitis.
Appendix. 1. Traumatic Ophthalmiae.
    2. Compound Ophthalmiae as the Catarrho-Rheumatic, Pustulo-Cattarrhal, etc.
    3. Intermittent Ophthalmiae.

Curiously enough, he proceeds, with no further ado, to describe the treatment of the ophthalmiae, or at least some general principles. First of all, he stresses the importance of finding the cause, local or general. Secondly, the eye must be protected from further causes of irritation. He then describes the various remedies. The first is blood-letting which was to be done by three different methods, venesection, the application of leeches and division of the inflamed conjunctiva.

Mackenzie was much against blood-letting in the treatment of Egyptian ophthalmia and further stated that he had never seen inflammatory disease of the eye cured by bleeding alone. When it had to be done, he recommended the removal of thirty to forty ounces of blood.

Scarification of the conjunctiva is done by making one or two deep incisions parallel to the lid edge. The lid is then alternately everted and allowed to fall back into position so that the divided vessels are refilled. Alternatively, a fold of conjunctiva can be lifted up and a snip made with a pair of scissors through a prominent vessel.

There is a very interesting sentence concerning the evacuation of the aqueous humour in certain kinds of ophthalmia as recommended by Wardrop. This, Mackenzie affirms, had never come into general use. It is interesting that in 1830, he did not see the significance of Wardrop's statement.

The second form of treatment was purgation. Evacuation of the intestines seems a far cry from treatment of an inflamed conjunctiva, but Mackenzie points out, very rightly, that besides reducing the fluid in the body, purgatives act on a mucous membrane lining the intestines which is anatomically continuous with that investing the eye.

The third remedy is emesis and the fourth diaphoresis.

The fifth remedy is by alteratives, principally mercury which he describes as essential to the treatment of the internal inflammations, especially iritis. He goes so far as to say that the latter would be incurable without mercury which acts as a sorbefacient, powerfully promoting the removal of effused coagulable lymph. He admits that its action is not exactly known, but he also remarks on the sad results when this form of therapy is omitted.

The sixth form of treatment is by tonics, cinchona being specially recommended for scrofulous ophthalmia, ranking in importance with mercury for iritis.

The seventh form of remedy is narcotics used to alleviate pain. It is recommended that laudanum be rubbed on the temple and forehead or taken internally. He regarded calomel taken with laudanum as almost specific for the rheumatic and catarrho-rheumatic ophthalmiae. 'A very peculiar set of Narcotics' is how he described belladonna, hyoscyamus and stramonium which were given in cases of iritis to dilate the pupil, chiefly as a paste rubbed into the skin of the eyebrow.

The eighth form of treatment is refrigerants, but Mackenzie uses it very seldom since cold applications lead to an uncomfortable reaction later.

The ninth form of treatment is astringents, but the only two he employs are silver nitrate and mercury muriate.

The tenth is stimulants and escharotics such as silver nitrate, mercury muriate, red precipitate, subnitrate of mercury, Vin. opii, etc., The first two were used in solution, never as ointment. He also used silver nitrate as an ointment, after some hesitation owing to its instability.

The last is counter-irritation such as blisters, issues and rubefacients.

It is clear that the pharmacopocia of 1830 was very scanty compared to that of today.

On the subject of catarrhal ophthalmia, he details all the signs and symptoms known to us today. The causes, he states, are atmospheric and are common in those who have to do night-watching and who are liable to wet feet. He relates epidemics for example, in the Duke of Modena's army in 1792 where the troops slept on straw in a convent facing to the north. Dust from the straw was considered the chief cause. Mackenzie was very firmly of the belief that catarrhal ophthalmia was contagious by means of fingers or towels and that those who thus contracted the disease had a more violent attack than the original sufferer.

He was of the opinion that the ophthalmia which attacked the British and French troops in Egypt was an atmospheric puro-mucous conjunctivitis, but that it later degenerated into a contagious, perhaps infectious disease, i.e. propagated by actual touch or by miasmata floating through the air.

He describes experiments carried out in Paris in 1820 in which the discharge from a case was transferred to the eyes of four blind children. As expected, they developed puro-mucous conjunctivitis. It is doubtful if anybody would care to carry out such an experiment nowadays.

Treatment of this condition is simple. He gives pride of place to local treatment rather than general remedies. He rules out blood-letting, but recommends a dose of calomel and jalap and determining to the skin by a warm pediluvium or by a small dose of spiritus minderi.

Lead acetate and zinc sulphate solutions are not recommended, but a solution of silver nitrate, 2–4 grs. to the ounce applied with a camel-hair brush, once a day, is considered more efficacious.

As a lotion, he employs 1 gr. of corrosive sublimate to eight ounces of water. This was applied milk-warm in a linen rag as a foment thrice daily. A few drops are then allowed to flow over the eye or syringed. At bedtime, red precipitate ointment is smeared over the eyelids.

He then describes contagious or Egyptian ophthalmia, the historic disease which led to the special eye hospitals in Great Britain. It had been brought back to this country in 1800–1802 by British troops returning from the Egyptian Campaign against Napoleon. Mackenzie was well versed in the variations of the severity and records that it was much more severe in the 54th (later the 2nd Battalion Dorset Regiment) than in the 52nd Regiment, (later the 2nd Battalion Oxfordshire Light Infantry) both English county regiments of the line, and less severe in the Chelsea Military Asylum than in either. He put this variation down to climate, temperature, the season of the year and the place of contraction of the disease.

The symptoms are very much as before, but haemorrhage occurs from the conjunctiva sometimes, the discharge becomes more uniform, chemosis is frequent, resembling the cowpox pustule between the ninth and twelfth days. The lids become very swollen and the cornea becomes involved in ulceration and very often perforation. This is clearly a description of gonococcal ophthalmia. In those cases which have suffered many relapses, the mucous cryptae of the conjunctiva of the eyelids and the meibomian follicles become enlarged. This is often given the name of Granular Conjunctivitis, but Mackenzie points out that there is no granulation involved, but that the enlargements are principally the acini of the meibomian glands enlarged.

He then describes how in some cases the granular conjunctiva may exist for months with the cornea vascular and nebulous without any purulent discharge and this accords closely with trachoma as it is usually seen and it is clear that the description of Egyptian ophthalmia as a purulent ophthalmia is of trachoma with a secondary infection with the gonococcus or vice versa and that the one has triggered off the other.

Mackenzie believed that the disease was propagated in the same way as catarrhal ophthalmia, but Ossalini attributed the spread in the French Army to the vivid light and heat of the country as predisposing causes and suppressed perspiration as an occasional cause.

In support of his theory, Mackenzie pointed out that the British troops introduced the Egyptian ophthalmia into the British Isles on their return and regiments which had never served in Egypt became affected and, in turn, carried it to other countries in which they served. It was his view that the low temperatures of this country combined with cleanliness prevented the ordinary catarrhal ophthalmia degenerating into the contagious variety.

The actual method of propagation, however, worried him and he pondered on whether miasmata arising from the eyes could cause its spread, but he pointed out that in an institution or regiment there was always evidence of actual contact. For example, each company in a regiment shared a barrack room and used the same towel, so that, even if they were scrupulous about washing their faces in clean water, they could all be infected by matter on the towel. He also quoted cases of accidental infection in two nurses, one of whom accidentally squirted fluid mixed with pus into her own eye and the other wiped her eye with the sponge she was using to clean the pus from a case of purulent ophthalmia. In both cases, the inflammation arose within a few hours.

Another illustration he gives which must have puzzled him was the tragic story of an attack of purulent ophthalmia in a French slave-ship, the *Rôdeur*. This left Le Havre on 24th January, 1819, and reached Africa on 14th March. The crew of twenty-two men enjoyed good health till they set sail again on 6th April. There was no obvious ophthalmia in the local inhabitants. There were one hundred and sixty negroes on board and, eighteen days after putting to sea, the first cases of purulent ophthalmia began to appear. The slaves were living in the hold, tightly packed, between decks. The crew at first ignored it since they thought that the redness of the eyes was simply caused by want of fresh air and water (only eight ounces a day and later only half a glass were allowed). The ship-surgeon advised an infusion of elder-flowers as a lotion and also fresh air and so the negroes were allowed up on deck in turns. The latter, however, had to be abandoned as the poor homesick and extremely uncomfortable negroes frequently embraced each other and flung themselves together into the sea. The disease spread with great rapidity and began to involve the crew. The first crewman to be involved was one who slept close to the grated partition which communicated with the hold. Next day, a young lad contracted the disease followed by the captain and most of the crew in the course of the next three days. The patients applied hot rice poultices and, when the rice ran out, they used vermicelli. They applied plasters to the back of the neck, at first cantharidis, but later pediluvia containing mustard, and exposure of the eyelids to the steam of hot water. Many became blind and there was a danger that the boat would not be navigated as far as the Caribbee Islands. One sailor however, escaped and all depended on him.

The *Rôdeur* fell in with a Spanish ship, the *Leon*, but they were in a worse state than themselves and neither could help the other. Gradually, however, some of the sailors began to recover and about the twelfth day were able to relieve those on duty. Some relief was obtained from dropping brandy into the eyes, but in spite of this, some had three attacks of the disease. As the swelling of the eyelids subsided, phlyctenules became visible and the ship-surgeon imprudently opened some of these, but so damaged his own eyes that he remained permanently blind.

On 21st June they reached Guadeloupe where a local negress recommended lemon juice in spring water as a lotion. This, combined with fresh provisions, worked wonders, but the only man who had escaped the disease on board fell victim to it in port.

The total number of totally blind was thirty-nine negroes and twelve crew. One of the latter was the ship-surgeon. Those who lost one eye were twelve negroes and five crew. One of the latter was the captain.

Mackenzie described this outbreak as being excited by atmospheric influence and spread by contagion. It was possible that the negroes already had trachoma and were infected with the gonococcus by the crew since there was no sign of purulent ophthalmia for the first fourteen days of the voyage. It would obviously spread very rapidly in the appalling conditions in the hold and would become more virulent. It would then be passed back to the crew in the form of purulent ophthalmia. Lack of fresh fruit and vegetables would also be a factor. Or perhaps the gonococcus lay dormant in the conjunctival sacs of the negroes until the overcrowding caused it to become more virulent.

The treatment he recommends in the first place is that already described for catarrhal ophthalmia, but in the later stages he uses blood-letting followed by leeches round the eyes and scarification of the conjunctiva, calomel and jalap or emeto-purgatives, or Dover's Powder as a diaphoretic. Calomel with opium until the gums are sore is recommended as general treatment.

In local treatment he uses alternately soothing and stimulating applications, but not one or the other alone. His grounds for this were the experiences of the French slave ship with the lemon and water lotion after the soothing and emollient treatment.

The eyes are to be syringed with a lotion of corrosive sublimate and a solution of silver nitrate instilled. If this is not successful, a solution of copper sulphate is injected over the surface of the cornea. Red precipitate ointment is placed between the lids at nights to prevent adhesion of the lids, but some prefer the citrine ointment.

Plasters at the nape of the neck or behind the ears are used as counter-irritants, steaming with hot water with laudanum or rubbing the head with warm laudanum or formenting the eyes with a warm decoction of poppy-heads are used as adjuvants.

Paracentesis is also recommended when it is thought that perforation of the cornea might be imminent, but Mackenzie was rather doubtful about its efficacy. Mackenzie lays down rules for the prevention of this devastating disease. In Egypt, exposure to the night air is dangerous and troops on ground or at bivouac should cover their heads well during the night. As soon as puro-mucous ophthalmia appears in a regiment, daily inspections by the medical officer are essential and should the disease be suspected, the patients should be promptly isolated. Excessive crowding together, especially in the dormitories, must be avoided and barrack-room communal towels abandoned. Basically, this was sound advice.

When he comes to describe iritis, he gives a detailed description of the signs and symptoms which could not have been bettered until the advent of the slit-lamp. As regards the causes, he enumerated exposure, transitions from heat to cold and other atmospheric changes giving rise to rheumatism: syphilis: strumous inflammation of the cornea with secondary iritis or primarily strumous: according to the Germans, arthritis due to gout and finally trauma, such as the operation for cataract.

He mentions the cornea looking as if it had been breathed upon so that he was familiar with endothelial bedewing although, of course, he would not be able to locate it exactly. He also reports brownish spots at times which were probably keratic precipitates.

He also describes what he calls aquo-capsulitis which consists of opacities in the internal surface of the cornea like milky spots producing a mottled appearance and sometimes accompanied by lymph in the anterior chamber. He goes so far as to remark that the symptoms are very similar to those of iritis and that iritis can occur with aquo-capsulitis, but he does not go as far as to say that they are parts of the same condition which they obviously are.

Another condition he describes is inflammation of the lens capsule which again he admits is always accompanied by iritis and is again part of the picture of the latter. He describes it as always chronic and accompanied by blood vessels crossing the pupil. As regards treatment, he strongly urges dilatation of the pupil using belladonna for the purpose. He employed an extract smeared on the eyebrow and upper eyelid every evening. He was very conscious of the need for systemic treatment and recommended blood-letting, not from the eye, but from the arm, purging, and antimony as a nauseant to render the body more susceptible to treatment by mercury and to moderate the circulation. The mercury was given to subdue the inflammation and prevent the deposition of lymph in the pupil. Of the various causes of iritis he describes rheumatism, for which he strongly recommends cinchona and syphilis in which he describes two signs described by Beer, namely upward and inward displacement of the pupil and condylomata sprouting from the iris. Mackenzie, however, had seen the former in other forms of iritis, but concedes the latter.

The chief drug for syphilitic iritis was, of course, mercury and Mackenzie reports the use of oil of turpentine in addition.

Another cause of iritis was scrofula and, according to the Germans, arthritis which they regarded as gouty. Mackenzie rather doubted this, but pointed out that gout was uncommon in Britain except in the opulent and lascivious whereas in the wine countries even the poorest indulge in much wine-drinking and gout is much more common!

In his description of aquo-capsulitis as a separate disease, Mackenzie is describing keratic precipitates and aqueous flare. He quotes Wardrop as having recommended paracentesis which, he affirmed was a certain cure. Mackenzie, however, points out the difficulties attached to this operation in a painful inflamed eye. This is understandable when one realises that there was no anaesthetic available.

Like Wardrop he mentions sympathetic inflammation following trauma in the eye which has not received the injury, but he dismissed the subject in one and three quarter lines.

Cataract takes up ninety-two pages in the book. Mackenzie is greatly concerned with the differential diagnosis between incipient cataract and incipient amaurosis, an exercise rendered very difficult by the absence of the ophthalmoscope. In the course of his discussion, he brings up the puzzling condition of glaucoma which at that time was often referred to as the 'Green Cataract'. Mackenzie points out that the opacity in glaucoma is always greenish and seems to be situated at a considerable distance behind the pupil or even deep in the vitreous. Above all, however, he points out that the eyeball always feels firmer than normal to the fingers and, at last, the ophthalmologist was beginning to distinguish the two conditions.

Mackenzie was quite convinced that the pigmentum nigrum of the choroid was deficient in glaucoma and that this was frequently accompanied by dissolution of the hyaloid membrane.

In spite of the absence of the ophthalmoscope, Mackenzie advises young practitioners always to dilate the pupil with belladonna in order to view the whole lens. As causes of cataract, he enumerates old age as the commonest cause and injury as the next frequent. He also stresses heredity and exposure to the heat of furnaces.

He is careful to point out that an operation for cataract may not be successful due to the unhealthy state of the retina and quotes several foreign surgeons whose results show only about 50 per cent partial or complete success. He is scathing about the results of what he calls mere oculists being any better, 'Their ignorance of eye diseases being in general fully as great as that of general practitioners'. He records his disappointment with the results from operating on a squinting eye and was thus conversant with amblyopia ex anopsia.

The Treatise and Later Works

Mackenzie discusses the age-old question of the treatment of cataract without operation and, like so many before and since, he is thoroughly sceptical. He points out that some of the cures have been in cases of fibrinous deposit on the lens or of rupture of the capsule with dossolution of the lens by the aqueous humour. Some, he even thought, were cases of glaucoma which responded to treatment for this condition.

The non-operative methods he mentions are:

(1) Blood-letting and the use of mercury. These, he states, are more likely to be successful if the cause of the cataract is inflammatory or if it be spurious. Morgagnian Cataract is mentioned as a possible result of external irritation and might respond to this treatment.

(2) According to Ware, a few drops of ether once or twice a day, along with occasional friction with the point of the finger on the closed lid, have proved effective.

(3) Counter-irritation. Gondret employed sincipital cauterisation by the actual cautery or by an ointment of strong ammonia.

Not surprisingly, however, Mackenzie begged leave to doubt the efficacy of these remedies.

The method of operating recommended is not practiced nowadays. Mackenzie advises that the patient should be seated with the head resting against the chest of an assistant standing behind him. This assistant applies his index and middle fingers to the upper lid in such a way that the middle finger projects beyond the lid edge and rests lightly on the eyeball so as to prevent it rolling upward. The operator pulls the lower lid downwards with the index finger and rests the middle finger on the caruncle so as to prevent similar movement downwards or inwards. The instrument which enters the temporal side prevents abduction. If the operator is not ambidextrous, however, he records that the patient should lie down for operations on the right eye and the operator sit at his head or, alternatively rest his head on a pillow situated on the back of a chair and the operator stand at his head.

Three methods of operating are described, couching or displacement, extraction and division.

Mackenzie was fully aware of the dangers of disturbing the hyaloid membrane of the vitreous by forcing a lens against it and also of damaging the ciliary processes and even the retina and choroid. He reports some advantage in reclination, in which the lens is not simply displaced downwards, but is turned through a right angle in addition. The anterior surface now faces upwards and therefore the lens is not so liable to ascend into its former position as in simple downward displacement. Reclination, however, inevitably damaged the hyaloid membrane.

Extraction of the lens caused him some worry. He regarded it as the operation to be preferred if only it had not been so dangerous or so difficult of performance. As there were no local anaesthetics in 1830, one can understand at least some of the difficulties.

The complications he dreaded were escape of vitreous, subsequent prolapse of iris and panophthalmitis. It seems that attempts had been made to remove the lens through the sclera, but the loss of vitreous was too frequent and this method was abandoned.

Division is done just as it still is done and he recommends it as the preferable operation in patients under forty.

When describing extraction, Mackenzie weighs the advantages of the incision above or below and, on the whole, favours the former, but finally suggests a half lateral half inferior incision as being a good compromise. He feels that an inferior section allows the iris to prolapse too easily and will obstruct vision if it does not heal by first intention whereas the superior section makes division of the capsule very difficult.

For the incision he uses Beer's knife, which has a triangular blade with an angle of 17° between the back and the cutting edge. This knife is still in use, but has been relegated to humbler duties since the advent of the Graefe knife. No iridectomy was performed and the capsule was opened by a needle or small lance-shaped instrument. The lens was exposed by pressure on the lower lid by the thumb.

Mackenzie favoured inspecting the eye on the third day and allowing the patient to sit up on the fourth day. On the fifth day, a more thorough examination was made and in eight or nine days the patient was allowed to walk about a little in his room. He reported that Wenzel confined his patients to their backs for two to three weeks at one time, but that Phipps examined the eye on the first day and allowed the patient to get up. The length of time in bed is still the subject of controversy.

Mackenzie quite often applied no covering at all to the eye and simply used a shade provided that the patient could be relied upon to keep the eyes shut. He sometimes applied a strip of court plaster to keep the eyelids together which he removed in twenty-four hours and then left the eye uncovered or replaced the plaster with a strip of linen spread with simple cerate.

He recommends that a nurse or an assistant should sit by the patient constantly for the first forty-eight hours after operation and then during the next few nights.

He does not employ belladonna in extraction or displacement, but does so after discission. He smears the extract on the eyebrow and eyelids and only if the pupil does not dilate does he drop it into the conjunctival sac.

If the iris prolapsed after the section was made, he rubbed the eye through the upper lid and then quickly exposed the eye to the light, thus causing the pupil to constrict. If this were not successful, he tried to replace the iris with the curette and, if this were not successful he made a small snip in the prolapse whereupon the iris often slipped back into position. A routine iridectomy does not seem to have been employed as it is at present.

When the iris prolapsed later, about the fourth day, for example, he again recommended making a snip in the prolapse and also bleeding, leeches round the eye and a plaster behind the ear. Opium and calomel were given systemically. Mackenzie considered that prolapse of the iris was probably due to inflammation in the eye rather than to injury and employed these antiphlogistic remedies. As a local application to the prolapse, he used lunar caustic daily. Belladonna was not used on account of the danger of prolapse.

There is an interesting, but distressing description of a couching operation carried out by James Wardrop in 1813 which Mackenzie quotes in this chapter. The patient was a deaf and blind boy of fifteen who seemed to be quite reconciled to his operation. However, when pressure was applied to the eye, he became very violent and it was impossible to secure his head. A second attempt was equally unsuccessful, but he was finally immobilised in a wooden box which folded over his body and was fixed by circular ropes. There was naturally much difficulty in opening the eyelids and steadying the eye, but once the needle touched the eye he 'remained quite steady and his dreadful frenzy ceased'. One is apt to forget that there were no anaesthetics in those days, or for the next thirty-five years, and one must admire the patients who faced operations in these circumstances.

Mackenzie placed couching last in his assessment of the merits of the various operations. He regarded discission as the safest, which is not unnatural, and extraction next. One can hardly disagree with this statement and couching is never done intentionally now.

Like all ophthalmologists of his time, Mackenzie was much puzzled by glaucoma and, in his treatise, he traced the history of the term from Hippocrates onwards. The earliest attempt at a scientific approach to the problem seems to have been in the early eighteenth century when the eyes of Bourdelot, physician to King Louis XIV of France were dissected by Maréchal and the vitreous body was found to be yellowish in its anterior part in both eyes. Brisseau, who was well aware that glaucoma did not respond to the operation of couching, and fortified by the details of Maréchal's dissection, therefore announced that the vitreous body was the seat of glaucoma.

Mackenzie, after reporting the above facts, wrote that in glaucoma it was obvious that the opacity lay deep to the clear lens especially in an early case and was of a greenish colour, sometimes sea-green, apparently emanating from the depth of the eye. As the disease progressed, the green colour occupied the centre of the vitreous humor and finally looked as if it came from immediately behind the lens. He felt that Brisseau had jumped to conclusions on the strength of one dissection by Maréchal and carried out his own observations on several eyes.

Firstly, he found that the choroid was of a light brown colour without any appearance of pigmentum nigrum.

Secondly, the vitreous humor was fluid, perfectly pellucid and either colourless or slightly yellow.

Thirdly the lens was yellow or amber and perfectly transparent, or nearly so.

Fourthly, the retina showed no trace of limbus luteus or foramen centrale.

From these observations, he concluded that light was reflected from the choroid which, minus its pigment, was of a bluish colour. It passed through the vitreous and the lens, both of which were of a yellowish colour and so the green reflection was formed.

As regards the fluid vitreous, he writes that this must be due to destruction of the hyaloid membrane and a subsequent accumulation of aqueous humor in the eye. In his opinion, the hyaloid membrane was undoubtedly the site of the formation and the absorption of the vitreous humor. When the membrane is absorbed, a morbid secretion of fluid occurs in the retina which is not furnished with the apparatus to remove it and so keep the fluid in a state of equilibrium. This accounts for the firmness of the eye in glaucoma which may go on to stony hardness eventually. He thought it possible that the fluid state of the vitreous or, in other words, destruction of the hyaloid membrane and pressure by a superabundant quantity of aqueous fluid accumulating in the eye might be the cause of the absorption of the pigmentum nigrum. He was not prepared to be dogmatic on the subject, however.

Mackenzie was familiar with the shallow anterior chamber, but he ascribed this to an accompanying arthritis and the condition he described was similar to what we now call acute narrow-angle glaucoma, i.e. varicose vessels of a livid colour over the sclera and conjunctiva, dilated irregular pupil, opaque lens which is pushed forward so as almost to touch the cornea and sclera pearly white, racking pain in the eye and head and sometimes the teeth and vision finally abolished. This description still holds today except for the curious omission of haziness of the cornea until the later editions of his book.

He was also familiar with field changes in the later stages in which he describes the eye as sensible to objects placed on one or other side of the patient, while in every other direction it distinguishes nothing.

He describes the cause of glaucoma and suggests that inflammation may be the cause of destruction of the hyaloid membrane. The Germans almost always associated glaucoma with arthritis or, at any rate, with slow arthritic inflammation of the eye.

He felt that habitual use of tobacco and spirits operated in the production of glaucoma and that it was common in those who did much close work. He knew that in Breslau half of the patients with glaucoma were Jews, but that Scarpa, during twelve years of dissection in Pavia, had never found fluid vitreous.

He knew that it was a bilateral disease and that in its fully formed stage, it was incurable, but he suggested means to arrest the disease.

Since he regarded the disease as inflammatory, he recommended bleeding and purging and counter-irritation. He did not approve of calomel and opium. He advised rest of the eyes, a mild diet and abstinence from tobacco and alcohol and tonics such as precipitated carbonate of iron and sulphate of quina, the last in arthritic inflammation of the eye. Oddly enough, he recommends Belladonna used as a drop of the aqueous solution, morning and evening.

His most important suggestion for treatment was, however, puncture of the sclera and choroid occasionally since, he wrote, it relieved the accumulation of fluid in the retina. In its humble way, this operation was the forerunner of all the surgical attempts to reduce the intra-ocular tension. He recommended removal of the lens since it not only lessened the greenish appearance and improved the vision, but warned that it was not to be done as a routine since there was a danger of producing severe postoperative inflammation in the eye. He did, however, seem to be aware that the lens could be the cause of a rise of tension.

Esserine and pilocarpine still belonged to the future and these remedies to the modern ophthalmologist will seem puny, but the foundation was being laid and, although the cause of chronic glaucoma has not yet been found, there have been many triumphs based on the patient study of ophthalmologists in the nineteenth century.

As the ophthalmoscope had not yet been discovered, Mackenzie was on very uncertain ground in his theories about the causation of amaurosis. As remote causes, for example, he cites heredity, over-exertion of sight and exposure to bright light. He also blamed anything which would cause a tendency to sanguineous congestion such as insolation, rage, forced exertions of the body, excessive stooping, the abuse of wine and spirits, suppression of discharge or the menses and slowness of the bowels.

Poisons are also blamed for amaurosis. Those which may produce sudden onset of symptoms are belladonna and stramonium and one which may produce an insidious onset is tobacco. Exhaustion of the body e.g. from chronic diarrhoea, long-continued grief, prolonged suckling and typhus fever are also considered as causes of amaurosis.

The treatment is very much the same as in many other eye diseases: Depletion in the form of blood-letting and purging and the much admired mercury is used as a sorbefacient, promoting the absorption of effusions in the cranium. Emetics and nauseants were also used in the form of tartarised antimony, tonics such as cinchona and iron, stimulants such as camphor and nux vomica, antispasmodics such as opium, musk and valerian (occasionally), sedatives such as belladonna and aconite were also tried. The local treatment was by counter-irritation, sternutatories, stimulating vapours and electricity. The last was not held in great favour. The mode of application was chiefly by 'directing the electric aura against the eyes, drawing it from them during the insulation of the patient and sometimes by taking small sparks from the eyelids and integuments round the orbits'. The meaning of this is hard to understand.

Mackenzie's *Treatise on Diseases of the Eye* cost 21/- in 1830. The medical Press of the day reviewed it with great enthusiasm, giving it the 1830 equivalent of 'Rave Notices'. Six have survived from the *Edinburgh Medical and Surgical Journal*, the *Medico-Chirurgical Review*, the *London Medical and Physical Journal*, the *London Medical Gazette*, the *Lancet* and the *London Medical and Surgical Journal*. All say much the same, but that of the *Lancet* probably expressed their sentiments best. 'Notwithstanding the great number of books on the Diseases of the Eye which have been published in this country, a complete account of the affections of this important organ has been hitherto a desideratum in our medical literature. There exist, it is true, a few general works on the subject, but these, though certainly not without value, are too brief, or too little comprehensive; it is with great satisfaction, therefore, that we have perused the excellent and comprehensive Treatise of Mr. Mackenzie. . . . While the author has, with great industry and research, collected the statements and opinions of numerous writers, English and Continental, . . . he has also interwoven with them the result of his own observations and experience, in a manner which increases their value, and shows him to be thoroughly and practically acquainted with the diseases of which it treats. . . . The arrangement, which is chiefly according to the textures of the part, beginning with the external or accessory organs, and ending with the retina, is at once scientific and convenient, and the division is sufficiently minute, without being carried to the absurd extent, and involving the almost endless nomenclature in which some writers have delighted. . . . Although it is not our intention to give a detailed account . . . of the work, we shall notice a few parts of it here and there, in which the facts and opinions advanced by the author are altogether new. . . . The methods of treatment recommended are, in every case judicious, and appear to be founded rather on practice than on theory and rather on his own experience than on the reports of others. . . . We can most strongly recommend the work.'

Some of Mackenzie's medicine labels which were preserved along with many of his prescriptions by Dr William Brown, his assistant and later his partner.

The label for Eye Drops was attached to a prescription for Vinum Belladonnae and the next label to a 'Tinctura Anodyna Ophthalmica'. This consisted of liquorice root, opium, oil of aniseed, camphor and alcohol and was added to boiling water and the steam used for soothing a painful eye.

Reproduced by kind permission of the Misses Lochhead, grand-nieces of Dr William Brown, William Mackenzie's partner.

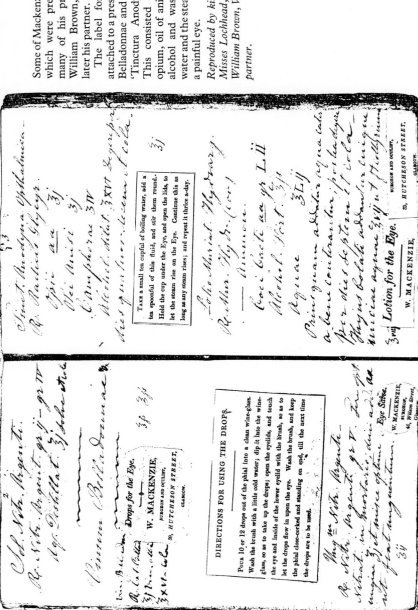

WILLIAM MACKENZIE
in his later years.

SOPHIA CHRISTINA NAPIER
about the time of her marriage to
William Mackenzie.

Reproduced by kind permission of Mrs Webster, grand-niece of Mrs Mackenzie

WILLIAM NAPIER

ELIZABETH RICHARDSON

Mrs William Mackenzie's Parents.

Reproduced by kind permission of Mrs Webster, grand-niece of Mrs Mackenzie.

CHAPTER 11

More Writings

THE *Treatise* was so successful that a second edition came out in 1835. Mackenzie wrote in the preface that he had been dissatisfied with the cross-sections hitherto produced, most of which, with the exception of that by Dr W. Soemmering, were very incorrect. He had requested his friend, Mr T. Wharton Jones to favour him with a magnified horizontal section of the eye and published this picture as an introduction to this second edition. In addition to the section of the eye, Wharton Jones produced drawings from which wooden blocks were made and these were produced in the course of the book.

Thomas Wharton Jones was a rather sad figure. He was an anatomist who worked with Dr Robert Knox, the unfortunate central figure in the Burke and Hare scandal. Like his chief, Wharton Jones was exonerated, but had to leave Edinburgh under a cloud of public disapproval. He was gifted with a great talent for drawing and came to Glasgow where he met William Mackenzie. The latter would admire him for he was a dedicated anatomist and was by now turning to Ophthalmology under Mackenzie's influence.

His father was Welsh, but he was brought up in Scotland and so spoke with a strong Scottish accent. His mother was Scottish and he was born in 1808. His father died when he was thirteen, but he went to Edinburgh University to study Arts and Medicine. At the age of nineteen he became assistant to Dr Knox, but he never liked to speak about this period of his life. He came to Glasgow in 1829 and met Mackenzie and Harry Rainy. He did a grand Continental tour in 1837, rather later than most, but it will become clear that his career was somewhat similar to Mackenzie's and they would be drawn towards each other. Mackenzie would be sympathetic towards the young Wharton Jones as he was himself an anatomist and had been presumably closely involved in body-snatching. He was rewarded by some very fine drawings, the outstanding one being the section of the eye. The description of the eye is not the same as it would be today. There is no iris muscle depicted and there is a membrane, for instance, called the membrane of Jacob connected with the pigment layer of the retina, which is presumably that known now as Bruch's membrane.

Wharton Jones went to London where he distinguished himself by becoming Professor of Ophthalmology at University College Hospital and numbered the young Joseph Lister amongst his clinical assistants. Like

Mackenzie, he was a prolific author and his book entitled *A Manual of the Principles and Practice of Ophthalmic Medicine and Surgery* written in 1847 was a success. It was beautifully illustrated by himself and ran to four editions, but poor Wharton Jones was not as successful as Mackenzie. He had an awkward manner and a caustic pen and nearly died of starvation in 1881. Private practice had not come his way as it might have done, and he was only saved from death by the intervention of his more prosperous colleagues and a Civil List pension. He died in comfort in 1891 in the Isle of Wight. As if he had not enough troubles, he was responsible for delaying the production of the ophthalmoscope, for in 1847 he was shown a prototype by Charles Babbage, an English scientist, but pronounced it as useless. The ophthalmoscope was produced by Helmholtz of Germany in 1851 and so Britain lost the chance of being the pioneer.

The second edition of Mackenzie's *Treatise* had grown to nine hundred and seventy-nine pages with the addition of a little material to each chapter and also some line drawings, mostly by Wharton Jones. These, in addition to the section of the eye which formed the frontispiece, numbered one hundred and there were additional chapters on extirpation of the eyeball, arcus senilis, anaesthesia of the parts supplied by the fifth pair of cranial nerves and entozoa of the eye.

He had obviously been thinking a lot about the greenish hue of the eye in glaucoma during the five years separating the two editions. He still described the same changes in the choroid vitreous and lens, but altered his theory of the causation of the greenish colour. 'It is not impossible', he wrote, 'that the appearance presented in advanced cases of glaucoma is not to be ascribed entirely to a reflection of the green rays of light from the amber-coloured lens, but partly to a reflection from the choroid at the bottom of the eye, that membrane being no longer capable of exercising its proper function from the defective state of the pigmentum nigrum.' He pointed out that there was no green surface in the human eye to reflect this colour as in the sheep, and it must be either in its entry into, or exit from the eye that it acquired the greenish hue and the most likely structure to modify it would be the lens. 'Were it proved that the retina, which is naturally somewhat bluish, supported by a choroid destitute of pigment and a whitish sclerotica, reflects the light forward into the eye of a bluish colour, then one of the principal phenomena of glaucoma might be regarded as no longer difficult to explain. In confirmation of this, if the lens is removed in this disease, or sinks to the bottom of the dissolved vitreous humor, the green appearance is almost entirely lost.' This reasoning, however, added little to his previous statement on the subject, but his views were carefully thought out and must have commanded respect in 1835.

The subject of sympathetic ophthalmia was still not extensively discussed, but in the second edition, five and a half lines are given over to it and Mackenzie states that it commonly occurs in scrofulous individuals.

The third edition was published in 1840 and cost 25/-. It ran to nine hundred and twenty-three pages and one hundred and twelve figures plus an appendage on the operation for squint of thirty pages. In addition, the pages were longer and the author estimated that had the smaller pages been used, there would have been one hundred and forty pages more than in the second edition. In his 'Advertisement to the Third Edition' he modestly begins by saying, 'The Demand for this Treatise on the Diseases of the Eye has been much greater than the author had any reason to expect. Since its first appearance, two large editions have been exhausted; it has also been reprinted at Boston in America, and a German translation of it has been published at Weimar.' He went on to say, 'The whole has again been carefully revised, and such alterations made as have been suggested by the author's continued experience, or by his perusal of the writings of others. He trusts that it will be found that, on every occasion, he had endeavoured to treat his fellow labourers in the same field with becoming deference and perfect fairness; never appropriating to himself the labours and improvements of others; but acknowledging openly what he has borrowed.' He certainly lived up to this principle and set his face firmly against plagiarism.

By 1840, Glasgow and the Clyde Valley had become a great industrial area and it is not surprising to find that the section of the book dealing with sympathetic ophthalmia had greatly increased in size. Penetrating injuries occurring in industry were becoming more and more frequent and the ophthalmologists of the day were alive to the dangers.

This section in the third edition, now covered eleven pages, Mackenzie illustrates the progress of the disease by quoting six cases treated in the Glasgow Eye Infirmary and they make depressing reading. The first injured one eye by a nail sticking out of a door and was treated for a whole year with multiple remedies, the most beneficial being, according to Mackenzie, leeches, calomel and opium and vin. opii applied to the eyelids. Belladonna failed to dilate the pupil and an artificial pupil was made, but the vision was finally lost when an intoxicated person struck him on the eye and produced a hyphaema which completed the disorganisation of the eye.

The second case was struck by a chip of cast steel. About a month later the other eye became involved and he retained a little vision in one eye.

The third was struck by a splinter of steel and the second eye became involved about seven weeks later. Little vision was retained.

The fourth was struck by a screw-driver. Almost six weeks later, the second eye became involved and the vision was finally lost in both eyes.

The fifth case was in a girl of fifteen who struck her eye on the latch of a door producing a prolapse of the iris. The second eye became involved four or five weeks later and the vison was lost.

The sixth case was struck on the eye by a chip of iron and the second eye became involved six weeks later. Two months after the injury a piece of iron was dislodged from the original eye after removal of a swelling over the injured cornea. His vision was largely lost.

These case histories are still typical of sympathetic ophthalmia as seen today, but, of course, cortisone has improved treatment greatly and the depressing visual results are not so often seen.

Mackenzie's conclusions also are very accurate. He describes the injury as most likely to be penetrating, but admits that occasionally the injury is not actually so deep, e.g. a blow on the sclera by a percussion cap and destruction of the cornea by sulphuric acid. He also admits that it is not necessary for the production of sympathetic ophthalmia that a foreign body be retained in the eye.

He thinks that injury to the lens has little or no influence on the production of the disease, but that prolapse of the iris is a common precursor and also injury to what he calls the annulus albidus of the choroid which was apparently part of the ciliary body. Cataract extraction, he reported, was in his experience, never a cause.

The average latent period between the injury and the onset of sympathetic ophthalmia he reported as five weeks and he was of the opinion that undue strain could bring it on, such as intense reading, and that the patients were very often in a poor state of health due to over-indulgence in spirits and tobacco. Mackenzie also describes the photophobia, dimness of vision and photopsiae which are known to be the earliest manifestations of the disease and ponders a lot over the cause thereof. He thought that the inflammation spread up the optic nerve, across the chiasma and down the opposite optic nerve. He quotes his old friend, James Wardrop, as the author of an article on iritis in one eye and then the other occuring in horses. The farriers of those days knew that suppuration in the first eye was unlikely to be followed by iritis in the second and, with great cruelty, put lime between the eyelids or drove a nail into the eye. In its humble way, this procedure paved the way to the opening of injured eyes, first of all those with a retained foreign body followed by a poultice, by which means a foreign body might be extruded. This led to a lessening of the danger to the uninjured eye and Mackenzie asked the question, 'Why should we hestitate to lay open an eye in which vision is extinguished, if the operation affords a hope of our being thereby able to save the other?' He was in fact, advocating incision of the cornea and even excision of a flap of cornea, even where no retained foreign body was evident. This was a step in the right direction, but several years were to pass before actual removal of the eye was practiced as a prophylactic measure.

There is little to add to the conclusions to which Mackenzie came in 1840 on the subject. The present day Ophthalmologist will not agree with his statements about an intra-ocular operation not producing sympathetic ophthalmia and there is no evidence that the infection travels up the optic nerve. Mackenzie had never heard of auto-immunity, of course, and this may have much to do with the aetiology, but we still do not know the exact cause of sympathetic ophthalmia and it is sad that even in Duke-Elder's *System of Ophthalmology*, Volume IX, published in 1966, it is still in the section entitled, 'Uveitis of Unknown Aetiology'.

The treatment has been improved with the advent of steroids, but Mackenzie's statement in 1840, that he had never seen an eye recover from sympathetic ophthalmia held good for most ophthalmologists for over a century. Once again, however, one can see the principles of prevention being laid down slowly by the great thinker, who gave the disease its name and who spent so much time pondering the problem.

Curiously, Mackenzie adds very little to the section on sympathetic ophthalmia in his fourth edition, published fourteen years later. He uses the same six cases to illustrate the cause and treatment of the disease although Glasgow had developed a great deal between 1840 and 1854 and had paid a high price for its prosperity from heavy industry in injuries to the eye.

The third case was reported to have asked for an artificial pupil to be made in 1842, but Mackenzie declined as both eyes were very soft. As regards treatment, he only adds that a little boy was greatly helped by potassium iodide after his mouth had been made painful by mercury and that the only case of sympathetic ophthalmia which he had treated successfully was one which followed a perforating injury by a packing case needle close to the edge of the cornea. He used calomel and sulphate of quina. Another remedy which he added in his fourth edition was inhalation of the vapour of sulphuric ether which, he thought, alleviated the symptoms markedly.

To return to the third edition, the main body of the book contained two new chapters, one on tumours of the orbit and one on aneurysms of the orbit. The appendix on the operative treatment of squint was published in 1841 and was attached to the third edition. The operation for squint had been introduced by Stromeyer only three years previously, although the Chevalier Taylor must be credited with suggesting some sort of operation on the muscle, but it is doubtful if he ever performed it.

Mackenzie displayed a very complete knowledge of the aetiology of concomitant squint. He knew that the refraction was usually unequal in the two eyes and, if it wasn't, the squint was probably alternating. He knew that the squinting eye could easily become amblyopic and that bandaging of the good eye could improve the vision of the squinting eye. He was familiar with the cover test and he knew that spectacles could help, but the practice was either to blur the good eye with a convex lens or to increase the vision in the bad eye with a concave lens on the surprising assumption that the aquinting eye was frequently myopic.

The operation for squint was, of course, tenotomy and was performed very much as it was in the twentieth century. The conjunctiva was lifted up in a fold and divided. A blunt hook was passed under the muscle and the tendon divided with scissors. Mackenzie was also aware that divergence might follow if too full a division of the muscle was made and if the muscle did not adhere to the globe anterior to the equator.

The fourth edition appeared in 1854 and by this time Mackenzie was able to report in the 'Advertisement' that, in addition to three British editions and the American and German editions, it had also been translated into French and Italian. He was much displeased, however, with the translations of Langier and Richelot from Belgium, who, he wrote, had executed the translation with great care and success; but the bibliographical references were entirely omitted. The original authors were therefore deprived of the share of credit due to them. Mackenzie was distressed that the readers of the French and Italian translations might attribute original observations to him rather than to the true originators.

This edition ran to 1107 pages and 133 figures and cost £1 10/-. Additional woodcuts for the illustrations had been provided by Dr John Ritchie Brown, Dr Wharton Jones by now being established in London. By this time, of course, the ophthalmoscope was in existence, but curiously enough, Mackenzie dismissed its use in a few sentences. When describing hyaloiditis, he writes that the ophthalmoscopes of Helmholtz, Coccius and Follin, 'are likely to assist in the detection of the effect of inflammation, both in the crystalline and in the vitreous body.' He is a little more expansive when writing on amaurosis. He admits that when the pupil is dilated with atropine it may be possible, by concentrating the sun's rays or the strong light of a lamp or gas flame by means of a convex lens on the interior of the eye to discover pigmentary depositories in the vitreous, effusion of blood or exudation of lymph on the surface or in the substance of the retina, or between it and the choroid, varicosity of the retinal vessels, partial removal of the pigment in patches, separation of the retina from the choroid in consequence of sub-choroid dropsy (by which he must have meant detachment of the retina), etc. The same, he writes, may be accomplished by means of the beam of light reflected into the eye from an ophthalmoscope. However, he goes on to say that such examinations may confirm an unfavourable prognosis already suspected, but one not likely to be satisfactory or safe in the early and curable stages of the disease.

Mackenzie was worried about the effect of the light upon inflammation of the retina. Hence his use of the ophthalmoscope only on cases which had been considered hopeless on various grounds. He did, however, change his mind, as he sometimes did. He was said to have been opposed to operating for squint at first, but later practiced it enthusiastically. So he came to use the ophthalmoscope.

The green cataract still troubled him and his thoughts on the subject had a more scientific note in the fourth edition. He wrote, 'The lens has become, in a certain sense, diplochromatic. The lens and the vitreous humor, which is also often yellowish in glaucoma, have the power of analysing the incident light, absorbing the violet, blue and red rays, leaving the yellow and green rays but little affected, so that they are dispersed, whence results the apparently green appearance of the humors.'

The great mystery of the green cataract, however, had not been solved, nor has it been explained yet. It is never seen now and authors have tried to explain it. The difficulty is that we can translate glaukos as green, grey or glistening and the hazy cornea of acute-closed-angle glaucoma could be certainly described as grey, but the nineteenth-century ophthalmologists actually saw the green colour and described it as even sea-green and the Germans called it 'Grünen star'. Yet it is never seen nowadays. Charles Snyder of Boston has suggested that the appearance was due to the yellow light from the candle, paraffin lamp or gaslight used in these days. The light they gave was quite different to the white light used nowadays. Colin Mailer makes the ingenious suggestion that the word glaucoma may be derived from the word 'Glaux' which means an owl, the dilated somewhat oval pupil resembling that of the owl.

Perhaps we shall never know the answer to these questions, but we know that Mackenzie's description of acute glaucoma can still hardly be bettered and that he puzzled over glaucoma until it made some sense to him.

After the third edition, the first French edition appeared. It was translated by Langier and Richelot and appeared in 1844. After the fourth edition, a second translation was made by Warlomont and Testelin and there was added an appendix which brought this book up to date, including as it did a description of the ophthalmoscope and its uses. This was published in 1856.

Mackenzie never stopped trying and he was busy with a fifth edition in 1866, two years before his death, but the French asked his permission to incorporate his notes in a further French edition. This was granted and they published these notes as a supplement in 1865 and he was to be allowed to translate it into English if he so desired. It seems doubtful whether he ever did so.

A German and an Italian edition were also made, the former in 1832, but the latter, for some reason, was never published. An American edition appeared about 1837 in Boston and in 1855 a further edition was published in Philadelphia which had an appendix similar to the French edition with particulars of the ophthalmoscope.

It will be seen that the first three editions appeared in the space of ten years, but fourteen years were to pass before the fourth edition appeared. Mackenzie, however, was not idle, for in 1841 there appeared a book on the *Physiology of Vision*. It appears that this book was not the success which one might have expected. George Rainy, Mackenzie's partner and Harry Rainy's son, wrote in Mackenzie's obituary that he thought that the subject was perhaps hardly so well suited to his particular prowess as those of a more practical kind. He did admit, however, that the book was far in advance of the age in which it was written. For all this criticism, it is a most interesting book to read now. George Rainy went on to say that those interested, on perusing it, will find how nearly he approached to distinct conceptions of truths which it was reserved for others to elucidate and establish. This was true. In his preface, Mackenzie wrote that he had been teaching Ophthalmology for over twenty years, but had never really had time to concentrate on Physiology and that this was the reason for the book which extended to two hundred and ninety one pages. He began by dealing with the physics of light and this extended to five chapters. He then went on to describe physics in relation to the mechanism of the eye and this is the part which will interest ophthalmologists looking back over the past one hundred and thirty years.

The difficulty facing the physiologists in 1841 was the mechanism of accommodation. Nobody had discovered any muscle tissue in the iris and ciliary body although several research workers had presumed its presence. The only definite muscular action they could see was the constriction of the pupil and they laid great stress on this in the mechanism of accommodation.

Four possibilities were considered:

(1) Elongation of the axis of the eye so that the distance between the cornea and the retina is increased.
(2) Shortening of the radius of curvature of the cornea so that its concavity is increased.
(3) Change in the figure of the crystalline so that its surfaces become more convex and
(4) Movement of the crystalline towards the retina.

It was thought that the elongation of the axis was brought about by contraction of the external ocular muscles. This would cause the aqueous humor to press against the back of the cornea and so cause an increase in its convexity.

The alteration in the shape of the lens troubled the observers of those days excessively. It was thought that it might be brought about by the action of the capsule or of the lens fibres themselves and Young proved that aphakic patients lose their power of altering the focussing power of the lens and they might be said to be on the right track. John Hunter, Young and others had already postulated that the lens fibres were muscular and Young noted that the ciliary nerves seemed to be more in number than could be accounted for by those which ended in the iris. He assumed that they went to the lens capsule, but Mackenzie was of the opinion that they went to the ciliary processes. Again, the evidence was accumulating and Porterfield postulated that the lens was pulled forward by the ciliary processes which he regarded as muscular. Mackenzie, however, pointed out that no muscular fibres had been found in the ciliaris ring or in the zonula ciliaris any more than in the iris, but he went on to describe the suspensory ligament of the lens as a corona of filaments extending from the posterior surface of the ciliary processes to the capsule of the lens and called it the orbiculus-ciliaris. He was worried, however, by the fact that the ciliary processes did not adhere to the lens capsule and therefore could not pull the lens forward, but, coming nearer and nearer to a solution, he felt that, if the lens were pulled forward, the filaments of this orbiculus capsulo-ciliaris might, by their elasticity, pull it back again. He also was of the opinion that as the pupil contracted, the ciliary ring expanded and so allowed the lens to travel forwards towards the pupil and that this change of position of the lens might be accompanied by a change in the form of the lens which became longer on accommodation and shorter on looking into the distance.

However, he quoted Sir William Brewster as stating that 'Although the most distinguished philosophers have contributed their optical skill, and the most acute anatomists their anatomical knowledge, yet, notwithstanding all their combination of science, the subject is as little understood at the present moment as it was in the days of Kepler, who first attempted the solution of the problem.'

Nevertheless, as one has seen, great thinkers like Mackenzie were gradually sifting the evidence and, as George Rainy had said, how nearly he approached to distinct conceptions of truths which it was reserved for others to elucidate and establish.

In the same volume a further separate booklet is included entitled, 'On the Vision of Objects on and in the Eye', which was added in 1845. In this he discusses another problem which exercised the ophthalmologists of those days, namely the cause of 'Muscae Volitantes'. Pitcairn was of the opinion that they could only be caused by lesion of the retina, but Mackenzie pointed out that a pin close to the eye causes a diffuse shadow, just as a 'Musca' does, which can be made sharp by viewing the pin through a pin-hole showing that the retina is still healthy.

The absence of the ophthalmoscope, of course, prevented any direct view of the opacities, but Mackenzie finishes the discussion with a forecast of the truth and quotes Alpinus, Young, Wardrop, Weller, Andrea and Brewster as being of the opinion that 'Muscae Volitantes' resided in the vitreous. The advent of the ophthalmoscope confirmed this view.

Shortly after the publication of the *Treatise* in 1830, Mackenzie wrote a little pamphlet entitled, *The Causes of Loss of Sight, Shortly Stated and Explained*. This was produced in 1832 and seems to have been something in the nature of an attempt to educate general practitioners and possibly even the general public, concerning possibly dangerous diseases. Vaccination was at that time busily engaged in preventing smallpox which had been a prolific cause of blindness and Mackenzie gratefully acknowledges the fact. The first paragraph describes ophthalmia neonatorum coming on on the third day after birth. This arose, wrote Mackenzie, from carelessness in not washing out the baby's eyes immediately and he reports that the poor in those days used some of the mother's milk. He recommends water without soap before anything else is done to the baby and also avoidance of too much heat, cold or glare being allowed to injure the eyes.

The second paragraph talks of contagious or Egyptian ophthalmia which he described at some length in his *Treatise* and which was clearly not the chronic type seen nowadays. Mackenzie estimated that one in five people, so afflicted, lose the sight of one or both eyes.

The third paragraph describes the commonest cause at that time of blindness in children which he calls inflammation of the membrane (i.e. conjunctiva) attended by the formation of pustules or pimples. This was sometimes called pustular ophthalmia and occurred between the teething age and the age of eight. The chief symptom, he states, was photophobia and the lesions often occurred on the cornea and might even perforate. This was a description of phlyctenular kerato-conjunctivitis and was much commoner in 1832 and apparently much more severe then than it is now. Mackenzie reported that drops of sugar of lead were used as treatment.

The fourth paragraph describes blepharitis marginalis which he admitted weakened the sight, but did not destroy it although it could cause the eyelashes to turn in and the eyelid to turn outward.

The fifth paragraph deals with injuries and contained a warning against improper treatment such as removing foreign bodies with an ordinary pen-knife. He advocated the wearing of protective spectacles made of wire-gauze such as fencers wore, for those in danger of serious injuries from flying particles. He also deplored the removal of foreign bodies by un-skilled amateurs.

The sixth paragraph describes the internal inflammatory conditions, such as iritis which causes blindness by closure of the pupil.

The seventh paragraph describes cataract both in the baby and in the elderly.

The eighth paragraph is concerned with failure in the sensitivity of the retina undiagnosable in detail in 1832 owing to the absence of the ophthal-moscope and lumped together under the title 'Gutta Serena'. This referred to the clear pupil presumably. Others referred to it as 'Amaurosis'. Mackenzie cites Milton as a sufferer from this. Later on, it was maintained that he had detachment of the retina when the ophthalmoscope made the latter diagnosable. In Mackenzie's time, it was a matter of academic interest only.

The causes of gutta serena, he wrote, were numerous. One of those, he asserted, was over-use of the organs of sight and man was never meant to look at small objects constantly. Mackenzie advised people to desist from too much close work and go out into the fresh air and look into the distance. (Judging by the amount of reading and writing that Mackenzie did in the course of his long life, he did not take his own advice too seriously.)

Other causes, he asserted, were blows on the head, excesses of tobacco or alcohol, want of sleep, mental depression, long affections of the stomach or bowels, close confinement, employment necessitating stooping, e.g. shoe-making and omission to wear reading glasses after the age of forty-five The whole pamphlet seems to have been a plea to the public or those in charge of first-aid rooms to employ expert help in eye conditions and not to rely on inexpert methods.

Mackenzie's contributions to medical journals were legion and a list recorded in 1833 when he was only forty-two, comprised thirty-two articles. The subjects were certainly not all ophthalmological. The first on the list, included in those which he had contributed to the *Quarterly Journal of Foreign Medicine and Surgery* which he had helped to establish with James Gordon, was a report of his interview with Antonio Scarpa which made such an impression on him in 1817. Also included was a description of the Vienna Medical School and reviews on various articles by other surgeons (Bock on the fifth Cranial Nerve, Cloquet on the Pupillary Membrane, Rosenthal on Surgical Anatomy, Demours and Beer on Diseases of the Eye, Marjolin on Anatomy and Schindler on Iritis). The last recorded article in this section was 'An account of the new views of the animal kingdom, which have lately arisen in the French School of Natural History'. This was something of a departure from Ophthalmology.

He records only one publication in the *Edinburgh Medical and Surgical Journal* and this was 'On the Symptoms and Cure of Croup'.

In the *London Medical and Physical Journal* there are five listed; 'On the asserted muscularity of the arteries. On closure of the pupil in Iritis, on the efficacy of Secale Cornutum in expelling coagula from the uterus, on representations of the eye, and on artificial pupil and on catarrhal, rheumatic and catarrho-rheumatic ophthalmia'.

Only one article is recorded in the *London Medical and Surgical Journal* for 1831 and this was entitled, 'On Nitrate of Silver Ointment.'

Not surprisingly, there are eleven items recorded in the *Glasgow Medical Journal* (Volumes 1, 2, 3 and 5). The first is an appreciation of his late colleague, Dr George Monteath who died in 1828 and was co-founder with him of the Glasgow Eye Infirmary. Most of the other articles were ophthalmological, but there is one entitled, 'A sketch of the natural cure of diseases' and there is another entitled 'Hints regarding the utility of Tonic Treatment in Infantile Hydrocephalus.'

Amongst the ophthalmological articles are, 'On the utility of Sulphate of Quina in Strumous Ophthalmia', 'Review of Carmichael on the use of Turpentine in Iritis', and 'On Glaucoma'.

In the *London Medical Gazette* there are three articles recorded, all ophthalmological and including a description of a case of foreign body adhering to the cornea and a case of living cysticercus in the anterior chamber. There is also an article on the 'Muscle of the Lacrymal Sac'.

Mackenzie's articles to medical journals went on and on. One of the most interesting was one on 'Post Febrile Ophthalmitis' written in 1843 and describing in great detail the mysterious epidemic which visited Glasgow in that year for the first time. It was similar to one which occurred in Dublin in 1826 and consisted essentially of a relapsing fever accompanied by inflammation of the eye. Mackenzie described it all with his usual thoroughness, but one is left in the end without a diagnosis. The fever was clearly very contagious and was evidently confined to the overcrowded areas where poverty and dirt prevailed. There was severe vomitting followed by great prostration and pains all over the body, but this only lasted for four or five days when the fever subsided only to relapse once, twice, or even three times. The eye symptoms came on several weeks later and consisted in a severe drop in vision followed by anterior uveitis and pain, as one would expect. Mackenzie discussed the differential diagnosis and excluded typhus, typhoid and cholera. He even considered malaria and syphilis and as jaundice was sometimes a symptom, yellow fever. In the light of modern knowledge, it is still difficult to come to a diagnosis.

Brucellosis, Weil's disease and toxoplasmosis could not be described as highly contagious and one is left little wiser than William Mackenzie in 1843, but the description of his investigations is something of an education. The tongue was closely inspected and described, 'Not much loaded, but rather clean; after a time it becomes brown and dry.' The skin was described as being 'Covered with a clammy disagreeable perspiration'. He described the result of venesection. 'The blood drawn from a vein is in only a few cases, buffy.' As regards the eye condition, he felt sure that there was inflammation of the choroid and retina initially which would account for the defective vision which preceded the inflammation of the iris.

In 1857, he published the report of a case of blepharospasm which he treated with inhalations of chloroform. The latter had been introduced ten years previously and had played its part in revolutionising surgery, but it was not usual to use it to treat photophobia and blepharospasm. The patient was a young woman who had suffered from phlyctenular disease and had been unable to stop herself from closing her eyes and rolling them upwards ever since. She was an inmate of the Blind Asylum and had been unable to open her eyes for sixteen months. Mackenzie had already tried ether for painful conditions of the eye ten years previously and decided to try chloroform in this case. He gave the chloroform at intervals of three or four days seven times and her conditon gradually improved. Mackenzie decided that the anaesthetic in the blood acted on the nervous system and the facial nerve in particular, but he admitted that, in spite of numerous theories, they knew nothing of the action of chloroform and other narcotics on the blood or on the nervous substance. Still, it was an original form of treatment, especially in 1857.

CHAPTER 12

Academic Activities

WILLIAM MACKENZIE was a good lecturer and his notebooks, which are still in existence, show that he had large classes in the College Street School for Anatomy and Surgery. In his first session 1819–20, fifty-seven names appear, but James Armour, already qualified, appears twice. In spite of this, this was a goodly number. The next session brought a record number of ninety-eight which again included James Armour and also Lennox Penthcind from Ireland and a William Jacobson from Yarmouth. In 1822, there were fifty-six including Ebenezer Miller from Edinburgh, Jacob Veisfeld from South Africa and James Matthew from Portugal.

He appears to have begun his Eye Lectures in 1820 and twenty-nine students appeared, including the faithful James Armour once more! A course on the Ear in 1822 attracted only three students, but a combined Eye and Ear course in 1823 produced eighty-two names, including W. E. Cook Clark from the West Indies. A course on the Ear, however, in 1827 attracted fourteen students.

Materia Medical lectures began in 1825 with thirty students which rose to forty-one in 1827, the maximum.

After this, only lectures on the Eye were given. Mackenzie was appointed Waltonian Lecturer on the Diseases of the Eye in Glasgow University in 1828 and devoted his time to these. The first session yielded fifty-one names, but for some reason, the numbers were thereafter very much smaller. It would almost look as if the students preferred extramural teachers. There are little remarks written in the notebooks such as, 'Not all got certificates', and 'Those who receive gratuitous tickets very rarely attend'. There is a sad one written in 1831. 'Ended 14.2.32. Cholera appeared on 11th'. Another dated 2.11.52 simply stated 'James Symington died of Typhus'.

Mackenzie apparently charged two guineas for these lectures, having been content with one guinea prior to his University appointment. This may have been considered too much by the students and may account for the small numbers. Both in 1842 and again in 1848 no course was given owing to shortage of applicants.

A prize for the best essay was instituted in 1837. The subject of the essay was not always recorded, but in 1850, Angus McWilliam won his prize for an essay on the muscular movements of the organ of vision and in 1851, John Ritchie Brown on the strucutre of the Tegumentary Membrane in general and of conjunctiva in particular. After the introduction of the ophthalmoscope, the prize was won for an essay on its use. Another subject which won a prize was Secondary Cataract and another the Internal Muscles of the Eye, a subject which gave rise to much controversy in those days.

Some of the future members of the Glasgow Eye Infirmary staff were members of his class. In 1833, Dr William Brown, who became a surgeon in charge of wards, and the next year one of the early clinical clerks, Hugh Kennedy attended. John R. Wood, who became one of the very early assistant surgeons attended two of his classes.

There were some interesting names amongst the students. In 1823, the name of a reverend gentleman, James McTear, was recorded and in 1834 no less a person than Le Baron Botsford attended the class. In 1839, a gentleman of the name of Albany Featherstonhaugh made his appearance. Neither of these last two gentlemen graduated in Glasgow and so, with their aristocratic names, which gave a tone to William Mackenzie's class, they must pass out into the unknown.

In 1833, Mackenzie's old chief in the Royal Infirmary died. Richard Miller had been lecturer in Materia Medica at Glasgow University and in 1831, the lectureship was upgraded to a professorship and Richard Miller became the first professor. Two years later, however, his retiral and death created a vacancy which was duly advertised and William Mackenzie applied. He had, of course, been lecturing on Materia Medica and had written a book on Therapeiology in 1826. He may even have foreseen this appointment and decided to write his book to support his claim.

The testimonials which he had printed, in support of his application, are preserved and they make impressive reading. Here are laudatory remarks from many very distinguished men. The first five are posthumous, beginning appropriately with one from the late Professor Beer of Vienna dated 25th November, 1817, and given to him before he left the Continent. It is written in Latin and speaks of his diligence and of his manual dexterity. His clumsiness at his first attempt at cataract extraction was, very properly, not mentioned! The next two were 'Thank you' letters from the late John Abernethy and the late Sir David Dundas for copies of Mackenzie's *Introduction to a Course of Lectures on the Diseases and Operative Surgery of the Eye* in 1818. Each added a small note of congratulation and expectation of fame in the future. The fourth was a second letter from Mr Abernethy certifying that Mackenzie had attended his lectures on Anatomy and Surgery. No less a person than Professor Richard Miller provided the fifth testimonial which he wrote in 1819 when Mackenzie came back to Glasgow. He referred very enthusiastically to his work as clinical clerk in the Royal Infirmary and then to his record in the Materia Medica class where, he wrote, William Mackenzie had headed the list in the class examinations. He added towards the end that he bore testimony to his correctness of moral conduct and that he was distinguished for the manners and all the feelings of a gentleman. This was written in 1819 in support of Mackenzie's application for the post of Professor of Anatomy and Surgery at the Andersonian Institute.

The sixth is an unusual testimonial by seventy-five students who attended his Anatomy class in College Street in the session 1821–22. It is a letter of thanks for his conduct of the class.

There then follow several from various professor and lecturers, Thomas Thomson of Chemistry, John Burns of Anatomy (Allan Burns' brother), Harry Rainy, at that time Lecturer on the Institutions of Medicine in Glasgow University, Andrew Buchanan, Professor of Materia Medica in the Andersonian Institution, William Davidson, Lecturer on the same subject in the Portland Street Medical School, James Watson, Lecturer in Midwifery in the Portland Street Medical School, James Brown, Andersonian Professor of Midwifery, William Auchincloss, Lecturer on Surgery in the Portland Street Medical School, James McConachy, Lecturer in Chemistry at the same school and James Adair Lawrie, Andersonian Professor of Surgery. Several of these recorded that they had personally attended Mackenzie's lectures on the eye and William Auchincloss even admitted to having repeatedly heard his lectures on Anatomy, Surgery and Materia Medica as well as on Ophthalmology.

The next testimonial is, interestingly enough, from medical practitioners who formerly attended Mackenzie's lectures over the previous fifteen years. They wrote that, 'As Mr Mackenzie is about to become a candidate for a Professorship in the University of Glasgow, we think it due to that gentleman, to take this opportunity of stating our high opinion of his fitness for such an office.' The testimonial later went on to say, 'He has attained in a very peculiar degree, the power of communicating knowledge. His mode of speaking is unembarrassed and animated, his style concise, perspicuous and elegant.' The signatures of fifty-two doctors are appended and include two of those who had given separate testimonials, namely, James Brown and William Auchincloss. Most of these men were in practice in Glasgow itself, but James Miller was in Maryhill, William Johnson in Edinburgh, James Paton in Paisley, along with other six, Francis Parker in Campbelltown (*sic*), William Lindsay serving in the Royal Navy, Hugh Patison in Renfrew and William Lorrain in Rothsay (*sic*).

The next group of testimonials comes from distinguished medical men whom he had met or with whom he had corresponded. This is perhaps the most interesting group of all, for here are some of the young men whom he met in the course of his travels, now come to maturity and, in some cases, to great distinction. The first was from Sir Charles Bell, a son of the Manse from Edinburgh, now aged fifty-nine and a Surgeon to the Middlesex Hospital. His testimonial was addressed to no less a person than the Lord Advocate, an old friend. He wrote, 'I am bold to say to your Lordship, that the best testimony to the capacity of a Professor is the proof he is able to give of teaching and forming a class of students by his unaided exertions. The success and promotion of such a gentleman does much to encourage others to follow his honourable and laborious course of life.'

The next testimonial was from William Lawrence, later to be created a baronet, who was a surgeon at St Bartholomew's Hospital. He knew Mackenzie when the latter was studying at Barts and was complimentary about his industry and referred to his *Treatise on the Diseases of the Eye* in very generous terms. Lawrence himself published a very similar and very fine treatise in 1833, the same year as he wrote his testimonial and he could have omitted any reference to Mackenzie's book. It was the same size as Mackenzie's, and lacked illustrations and an index. Lawrence was very distinguished, but inconsistent and very opinionated. He was on the staff of Moorfields as well as of Barts and Mackenzie may have studied under him there also. He was only eight years older than Mackenzie and was appointed to Moorfields at the early age of twenty-seven. He was the stormy petrel of his time at Barts.

The next batch of testimonials includes some from Mackenzie's old friends from his early struggling days and they make very interesting reading. There is one from Sir Charles Scudamore, now a knight and a Fellow of the Royal Society. 'Wee Scuddy' had turned up trumps again with a fine testimonial paying tribute to his abilities as well as his integrity. His address was given as Wimpole Street.

Another was from James Alexander Gordon, now Physician to the London Hospital, but writing of his association with Mackenzie on the Continent and in the formation of the *Quarterly Journal of Foreign Medicine*. He points out that, although they had been separated, he had never ceased to regard with the deepest admiration, the important and acknowledged services which Mackenzie had rendered to medicine. He felt, therefore, that he had a right to recommend him to the favourable notice of the University. Interestingly, he writes 'Mr Mackenzie . . . holds the inadequately remunerated office of Lecturer on the Eye in the University – he proposed and for nine years gratuitously attended the Eye Infirmary, now an important part of the Medical School – he projected, and for two years gratuitously conducted, the *Glasgow Medical Journal*'.

There is a very short testimonial from James Wardrop extending to only five lines, but, not unexpectedly, it is complimentary. He did not display his appointments and distinctions at the top of his testimonial, but he was having a very successful career. He had gone to London and Vienna, where he studied under Beer.

James Moncrieff Arnott also rallied to his assistance with a testimonial written in New Burlington Street. He was now a Surgeon Extraordinary to the Queen and Surgeon to the Middlesex Hospital. He went so far as to write that he knew no one who possessed a more thorough knowledge of every branch of medicine. Praise indeed!

The other testimonials were from further very distinguished people – Dr James Johnson, Physician Extraordinary to the King, written from

Suffolk Place, Pall Mall East; Dr John Ashburner, Lecturer in Midwifery at St Thomas' Hospital, who had studied for a short time in Glasgow, but was now living at 5 Wimpole Street. (He reported that he believed Mackenzie's work on the Eye to be the best book extant on the subject and the *Glasgow Medical Journal* afforded abundant evidence of his varied and extensive knowledge); Dr Roderick MacLeod, Physician to St George's Hospital; Dr Henry Earle, Surgeon Extraordinary to the King, Surgeon to St Bartholomew's Hospital and Professor of Surgery and Anatomy at the Royal College of Surgeons, then living at George Street, Hanover Square; Dr Samuel Cooper, Professor of Surgery in the University of London; Dr Edward Stanley, Assistant Surgeon to St Bartholomew's Hospital; Professor Robert Graham, by now Professor of Botany at Edinburgh University, but formerly the physician in the Glasgow Royal Infirmary who asked Mackenzie to bleed Granville Pattison; and lastly a very short testimonial of five lines from Dr James Macartney, Professor of Anatomy and Surgery in the University of Dublin. This last was, perhaps, the most uninformative of them all and suggests that he really knew very little about Mackenzie except by repute.

With such an impressive volume of testimonial, one could be excused for thinking that Mackenzie's appointment to the chair was certain. Here were paeons of praise from men who had known him as a student, as a post-graduate student in London and the Continent, as a travelling companion and as a lecturer. They had all, except Wardrop, set down their own qualifications and distinctions and then generously sung Mackenzie's praises. It was rather like the grand finale of a pantomime, with each actor in the play taking a bow and then standing aside to allow the audience to give the principal character a greater ovation. But alas, the appointment was not given to William Mackenzie, but to his old friend of the Paris days, John Couper, who had sat with Mackenzie and Moses Buchanan laughing over reminiscences of their student days. Perhaps, if he had been appointed, Mackenzie would not have found time to be so competent an ophthalmologist, or perhaps he would have somehow managed to fit it in to his busy working days.

William Mackenzie tried, rather unsuccessfully, to lecture on Medical Jurisprudence. He was unable to carry out the necessary experiments and prevailed upon James Armour to do them for him. This would be a new branch of medicine, but both Armour and Rainy took it up with enthusiasm. The former was the first lecturer on the subject in the Portland Street Medical School in 1826 and the latter, the second Professor in Glasgow University from 1841 to 1872. The chair had been founded only two years previously in 1839.

In 1833, William Mackenzie graduated M.D. He does not seem to have had this degree when he applied for the Chair of Materia Medica since it was not recorded in his application, but he must have had it soon afterwards. It would be a useful qualification for a would-be professor.

Another honour which came to Mackenzie was the conferment of the newly established and, at that time, rather controversial Fellowship of the Royal College of Surgeons in 1843. There were two hundred and ninety-eight names published then and all were already Members of the College. The company was a distinguished one and included two of his close friends, James Wardrop and James Arnott. Other ophthalmologists on the list were George J. Guthrie, who founded the Royal Westminster Ophthalmic Hospital in 1816 and Benjamin Travers, father and son, and William Lawrence, all of London. Mackenzie was the only one from Glasgow, but there were two Edinburgh surgeons, the famous James Syme, Lord Lister's father-in-law and James Duncan.

The controversial aspect of the election of Fellows was that there was to be an examination for entry after the initial three hundred-odd appointments and this was not considered a proper proceeding at all. There was a great deal of heart-burning from those who considered themselves as distinguished as those who had been chosen to receive the Fellowship and who would require to pass the examination if they still wanted to be Fellows.

Another sore point was that the subsequent Fellows were not required to be already Members of the Royal College of Surgeons as was the case in the sister Royal College of Physicians and there were other objections. However, the system survived and is still with us. The original three hundred-odd Fellows were apparently chosen according to definite rules. Firstly, every surgeon and assistant surgeon in every recognised hospital in England was chosen: then all lecturers and demonstrators in Anatomy and Surgery in schools attached to these hospitals: then Sir James McGrigor was asked to nominate distinguished navy surgeons and Sir William Bennett some more. The chairman of the East India Company sent in his list: lastly the Council added its own list of distinguished medical practitioners, mostly surgeons practising in London, but presumably including William Mackenzie since he would not come into any other category. A few of those chosen were general practitioners.

It seems to have been agreed that this selection of distinguished men for the beginning of the business had been done very well, but letters began to appear in the medical press from somewhat disgruntled surgeons, which is not surprising although, in some cases, probably not justified. There is some resemblance to the modern distinction awards, but without the confidentiality. One surgeon wrote a letter to the *London Medical Gazette* complaining about his omission from the list, which gave rise to a reply in the same *Journal* from another surgeon suggesting that, if only he had not taken part in practising mesmerism, his name would certainly have been included in the original list!

CHAPTER 13

Et Cetera

THUS DID fame and fortune come to William Mackenzie. Glasgow by now was a large industrial city sprawling westward like a giant amoeba. It was very prosperous too and the wealthy citizens began to build fine big houses farther and farther west and with them went the, by now, fashionable oculist.

Mackenzie did not always consult in his dwelling-house. Even in 1823, when he was living in North Albion Street, he occupied rooms at 242 George Street for consulting purposes for a year. This was the year of his first marriage and there may not have been enough room in the house. After all, a consulting room and another room which can be used for at least part of the time as a waiting room, taxes the accommodation in any house. It has been said that a residential district is beginning to go down the social scale when doctors move in and there is a grain of truth in this when one considers the extra room or rooms needed if a doctor is going to consult in his own house. One has only to trace the migration of somebody like William Mackenzie to support this view.

After leaving North Albion Street, he spent a year living and consulting at 46 Wilson Street, then the same at Spreull's Court in Trongate, but in 1829, when he went to live in George Square, he occupied consulting rooms at 39 Hutcheson Street. The move to the west was still on and we find him in 1841 living at 188 Buchanan Street, i.e. near Cathedral Street and in 1850, he took over consulting rooms five doors up at No. 198. The next move was much farther west, right out to Hillhead, in fact, to a lovely new house at No. 1 Oakfield Terrace. This was in what is now called Oakfield Avenue, but the first houses were in a little terrace between Gibson Street and University Avenue. Mackenzie's house was at the corner of Gibson Street and is now no more, its place being occupied by the Stevenson Recreational Buildings of Glasgow University. He retained his consulting rooms in Buchanan Street at first, but soon moved to rooms in a house at 49 Bath Street. This was on the south side of the street near the corner obliquely opposite the Corporation Transport Offices. These rooms were shared by his assistants, William Brown and George Rainy. The latter stayed on after Mackenzie's death until his own a year later, and then Thomas Reid occupied them. There was a good deal of goodwill attached to the consulting rooms of the great in those days and Thomas Reid certainly became quite famous on his own account.

The migration of the specialists westward continued after Mackenzie's death and we find them living in West George Street and Blythswood Square. Then they began to appear in the Charing Cross area and this became the consultants' and specialists' mecca and, between the Wars, became almost entirely occupied by the profession from Park Circus down Woodside Crescent across Sauchiehall Street as far west as Kelvingrove Street. But times change and the specialists have scattered. There are still several consulting rooms in the area, but almost all the consultants live elsewhere.

William Mackenzie's middle-age was fully occupied with practice. He had become the fashionable ophthalmologist and patients came long distances to consult him. He was apparently incapable of charging large fees and he seems to have done his own dispensing. Certainly there are several of his labels still in existence with his name and address printed on them. Some are for bottles and others are for the small cylindrical ointment boxes then in vogue. Freeland Fergus records that, on one occasion, a wealthy patient travelled half across Europe to consult Mackenzie and proffered him a golden sovereign. Mackenzie solemnly handed him 16/6d change and a bottle of eye lotion. Long before he became famous, Harry Rainy put down his lack of success in London to this inability to charge large enough fees.

On his desk, he kept a copy of his book which had been specially printed with blank leaves between the printed pages and these he used for taking notes for future editions. This copy which was, in fact, in two volumes owing to the increased bulk, is still in existence in the library of the Royal Society of Medicine and one can trace the problems and how he dealt with them to the best of his ability.

Honours came to him too. He was asked to be a corresponding member of many continental and American ophthalmological societies. On 3rd March, 1838, he was appointed Surgeon Oculist in Scotland, in Ordinary to Queen Victoria. This must have made him very proud and he would be charmed by this honour from the young Queen who was then still only eighteen years of age and not yet crowned. Mackenzie was the first Scot to hold this appointment and there have been six other distinguished oculists to hold it since then, namely:

William Walker	— —	(1870–1885)
Douglas Argyll Robertson	— —	(1886–1913)
George A. Berry	— —	(1914–1928)
Arthur H. H. Sinclair	— —	(1929–1951)
John Marshall	— —	(1952–1962)

and George I. Scott, who is the present holder.

As the years passed, however, he must have felt lonely and he turned his thoughts towards matrimony again. His health was not as good as it used to be and he spent several weeks in bed each winter suffering from bronchitis. By about 1852, he stopped going to the Eye Infirmary, but he only stopped lecturing in 1862, although his cough was irritated thereby. However, matrimony appeared to be the proper procedure to him and his choice fell upon Miss Sophia Christina Napier of 99 Douglas Street. She was, at the time of their marriage in 1854, aged thirty-five, the eldest of a family of seven girls and one boy. With one exception, they were a very musical family, which is understandable as their father, William Napier, was a teacher of music and Sophia taught music also. William Napier came from the North of England where he taught music to private pupils. Fate decreed that he should be engaged by Mr John Manson, a gentleman of some substance, to give piano lessons to his ward and niece, Miss Elizabeth Richardson. Like so many young girls, Elizabeth fell in love with her music master and, knowing that her guardian would strongly disapprove of such a marriage, the couple secretly made plans and eloped to Edinburgh. Alas, the romantic aspect of the affair was lost on Mr Manson who never forgave Elizabeth and, as she had been made a Ward in Chancery, he promptly disinherited her. There is no evidence of Mackenzie's love of music, apart from a reference in his Continental diary to his having bought a copy of the music of a Swiss national song when in that country. No romance born of a mutual love of music can be invoked therefore.

All was arranged with due decorum and William Mackenzie drew up an ante-nuptial settlement in August 1854, and on 12th December, 1854, they were duly joined in matrimony by the Rev. Archibald Nesbitt, minister of St Stephen's Quoad Sacra Chapel of Ease in Cambridge Street, Glasgow.

They took up residence in their new house at No. 1 Oakfield Terrace and almost four years later, Mrs Mackenzie bore him a son, William James. By this time, 8th March, 1858, Mrs Mackenzie was aged thirty-nine and her husband almost sixty-seven.

In 1859, when he was aged sixty-eight, William Mackenzie was honoured by the Directors of the Glasgow Eye Infirmary with the presentation of his portrait in oils. He had never accepted any honorarium for his services there and the Directors had put the money away. After thirty-five years, quite a sum would be available and Glasgow's foremost artist, Daniel McNee was commissioned to paint the portrait. It was duly presented to him on 6th October and it cost £84 10/-. It is an excellent portrait and it has hung in the Eye Infirmary for many years as if he were still watching the work which he began so long ago.

As he grew older, William Mackenzie began to suffer from chest pains, but he continued working at his consulting rooms in Bath Street. On 15th July, 1868, he operated on a patient for cataract with his usual skill and on 29th July he performed the operation of keratonyxis, or puncture of the cornea, presumably for a corneal abscess. Later that day, he felt unwell and left his consulting rooms early. However, he called at the Faculty of Physicians and Surgeons' Library in St Vincent Street and took out a French book, Volume 32 of the *Encyclopédie des Sciences Médicales* which was found with a book-mark at page 390 at an article entitled 'Mémoire sur l'angine de poitrine'. That night he was seized by severe precordial pain and his medical adviser, Dr Stewart was called to his bedside. The latter recorded that his pulse was very irregular, being interrupted after ten pulsations. Mackenzie asked for chloroform for the pain, but in the early hours of the morning of 30th July his eyes became fixed, he shook violently and died.

Curiously, this description of his death was given by Dr Warlomont in a very fine obituary notice in the *Annales d'Oculistique* and it is much more detailed than any in the British literature.

In spite of his apparent unwillingness to charge large fees, William Mackenzie left £34,624 4s 2d, quite a large fortune for these days. Very properly he made provision for his wife and son in his will. Broadly speaking, he left the rent, use and enjoyment of their house to his widow. In addition, he gave her permission to sub-let it if she so desired. To his son he left his microscope, his apparatus, his preparations and the copyright of his books. The residue was to be divided between his widow and his son. In addition to her half, the widow was to receive the favours set out in the Marriage Contract made in 1854. These included the Widow's Pension from the Faculty of Physicians and Surgeons, to which she was entitled since her husband had paid his fee for becoming a Licentiate. They also included the household furniture, table-linen, silver plate, china paintings and wines, but not his professional apparatus or books. £40 were to be put aside for mourning and £3,000 were to be paid to her. Miss Napier, for her part, assigned all her heritable and moveable means to her husband-to-be.

His interest in what the inventory described as 'The business of surgery by him and George Rainy at 49 Bath Street' was valued at only £150 and one half of the furniture there at only £22 8s 10d. A sad little promissory note by T. Wharton Jones dated 27th April, 1844, was found amongst Mackenzie's effects and recorded in the inventory. It was for £180 and was payable twelve months after its issue. It seems that it was never paid for the document mentions interest of £209 5s 5d making a total of £389 5s 5d. For the purposes of the Estate it was valued at 1/- in the pound, i.e. £19 9s 3d.

He did not, however, forget the study of Ophthalmology in his Will and he decreed that, on the death of his widow, and after legacies of £100 each to his cousin's sons, and £200 to his widow's sisters, £5 were to be paid to the Glasgow University to buy eye instruments or other prizes to medical students provided that the lectures on the eye were officially part of the medical curriculum. He also left money to pay the lecturer or professor £100 per annum on condition that he gave fifty lectures annually. If the University did not prove to be willing to establish this lectureship, the latter was to be established at the Glasgow Eye Infirmary, the lecturer to be chosen from the surgeons or assistant surgeons there.

William James Mackenzie did not reach old age, for he died at the age of 42 at 6 Hawthorn Gardens. He had been married twice, firstly to Charlotte Mary Perryman in 1883 and secondly to Clara Mayo Elliot in 1895. He did not follow in his father's footsteps and is described as an electrician at his first marriage and as as a master photographer at his second.

Mrs Mackenzie, however, survived both her husband and her son and died at No. 1 Oakfield Terrace on 20th September, 1902, at the age of eighty-three.

When all is said and done, it is much easier for the biographer to record what a man did with his life than to try to assess the influences which made him do what he did and what sort of man he became thereby.

William Mackenzie belonged to the privileged class of his day. He was born in a big house in the fashionable quarter of Glasgow in 1791 and he was able to go to the Grammar School and then the University. He did not graduate in Arts even although he studied for his degree nor did he complete his Divinity studies, but his father's estate was seemingly able to pay his fees in the Medical Faculty. Mr James Mackenzie was evidently a very religious man and, when he died in 1805, a small obituary notice appeared in the *Glasgow Herald*: 'On 9th curt., Mr James Mackenzie, Merchant, known to many for exemplary piety and zeal for the interests of Christianity. While they regret his departure, it will be satisfactory to those at a distance to learn, that the close of his life was to him remarkably peaceful and free from pain. He appeared elevated above the world, a just entering to a blessed mortality.' Even allowing for the exaggerated language of the day, this is a highly complimentary description of his father and he recalls him in his Continental Diary. He never mentions his mother and it may well be that she died when William was very young.

He must have been a bright boy as he went to the University at the age of twelve and he already had a very good knowledge of Latin and Greek. He prefaces one of his articles with a passage in Greek from 'Epicteti Dissertationes Ab Arriano Collectae'. In this passage, the author questions whether those who dare to open surgeries really know what actions the various medicaments have. He seems to be addressing any who aspire to becoming lecturers too light-heartedly and uses medicine as an example. It would seem that study at a University in those days would be regarded as an extension of schooling, but even allowing for that, he had a very extensive University career lasting in all twelve years and in three Faculties at that.

It is impossible to say whether his religious doubts about the Story of the Creation made him into an agnostic. There is one letter from Gordon expressing satisfaction that he went regularly to church and certainly the Rev. Adam Boyd was one of his most assiduous correspondents. Gordon, however, suggested that his church-going would conduce as much to his respectability as to his happiness and comfort! He also hoped that Mackenzie would not adopt a Chalmerian style in his lectures, referring to the famous preacher of those days. If only Adam Boyd had desisted from writing his letters and then covering them with more writing at right angles, we might have read more about this aspect of Mackenzie's life. Some of Mackenzie's writings have a religious slant, for example, when he wrote his pamphlet in support of an Eye Infirmary in Southwark, and he was married on both occasions by a clergyman. He belonged to a generation which, on the whole, believed in the Bible *in toto*, but some were beginning to think along different lines and Charles Darwin shocked the religious leaders of the day during Mackenzie's lifetime with his theories of natural selection and his 'Origin of Species'. It seems that this made Darwin into an agnostic for a time, at any rate, but one must admit that William Mackenzie's views are unknown.

His medical studies were also extensive as a student since he chose to do a clinical clerkship in the Royal Infirmary rather than an apprenticeship to a general practitioner. This would be done against the background of the Napoleonic War, but he was qualified too late to take any part in this. His colleague, George Cunningham Monteath, however, was a little older and was Medical Officer to Lord Lovain's Northumberland Regiment of Militia and many Glasgow doctors were similarly engaged, presumably on home defence duties only. Mackenzie, however, saw France and other countries at first hand shortly after the war ended and duly recorded his impressions in his Diary. He was to refer to the horrors of war in his famous pamphlet on the provision of subjects for dissection and the whole episode of the war would leave a deep impression on him.

There was disappointment in his life too. When he wrote his article on the Lacrymal Organs in 1818, the editor went bankrupt and part of the edition was seized by his creditors and even sold as waste paper. This was not encouraging for a young man of twenty-seven at the outset of his career.

The London episode was a great disappointment too. His inability to amass a private practice and to establish an Eye Infirmary in Southwark must have saddened him, but he knew that he was a good lecturer and the worst blow, perhaps, was his failure to win a lectureship on Anatomy. So he came home to Glasgow.

There was grief in his life too. The nineteenth-century people were no strangers to untimely death with smallpox, typhus, cholera, tuberculosis and typhoid taking their toll. He lost his parents when he was a boy and his first wife before she reached middle-age. His little daughter died before she was three and his friends, George Monteath, James Armour and George Oswald Sym were all young men when they died.

As always, however, destiny played its part. Had he followed his first intentions and graduated in Divinity what would his destiny have been? Would he have occupied the pulpit of a little church in the country, satisfying his restless brain with exploring the geology of the good earth and studying the story of the creation again? Would he have developed into a great preacher just as he developed into a great lecturer or would he have embraced the academic life and held a Chair in a Divinity Faculty somewhere?

Had he been more successful in London and had gained the lectureship in Anatomy which he wanted, Southwark might have had its Eye Infirmary in 1819 and Mackenzie might have become a fashionable London ophthalmologist.

But destiny pointed to Glasgow and the dissecting rooms there. Had it not been for his admiration for Beer in Vienna, he might have stayed an anatomist, but destiny again brought him to George Monteath and the Glasgow Eye Infirmary was born. Thus was his fortune assured and the great ophthalmologist emerged. But this might never have happened if Granville Pattison had not been involved in a scandal. Thus does destiny work.

Josef Beer was not the only man who influenced Mackenzie, but he was the one who awakened fully his interest in ophthalmology. Antonio Scarpa impressed him very much, but he was primarily an anatomist and his book on Ophthalmology was a small one. Roux and Dupuytren gave him much teaching in general surgery in Paris, building on the foundations laid by Abernethy in London. Richard Millar in Glasgow gave him his early training in general medicine and it was towards his Glasgow colleagues that he turned as time went on. Mackenzie must have felt lonely sometimes for, in an age where large families were the rule, he seems to have had few relatives, and it would be natural for him to discuss his problems with his contemporaries. Chief of these was Harry Rainy, half of whose ancestry was from North-east Scotland and half from the West Highlands, son of the manse and wise counsellor. Many turned to him for advice and few were disappointed.

These, then were the happenings and the people which helped to form his character. It was not a very complex one, for he was a simple man. George Rainy, son of Harry and Mackenzie's partner latterly, wrote his obituary notice in the *Glasgow Medical Journal* and M. Warlomont, the Belgian co-translator of Mackenzie's Treatise into French wrote one for the *Annales d'Oculistique*. Both knew him well. Later Freeland Fergus, who had been at school with William James Mackenzie wrote an article on Mackenzie in the *British Journal of Ophthalmology* in 1917. He had only a vague recollection of meeting William Mackenzie in his old age. Curiously enough, it was Warlomont who gave the most detailed account of his personal habits and his appearance. He reported that he was small, bald and prematurely grey. He also reported that he was myopic in one eye and emmetropic in the other. When he came round to using the ophthalmoscope he used the Jaeger model with the indirect method with a $+8.0$ D as the ocular lens. For ophthalmoscopy he used his presbyopic eye and his myopic eye for reading and operating. He did, however, use a small reading correction in artificial light. Warlomont went on to say that Mackenzie had blue, penetrating eyes and a large forehead. He described

× the diseased lens & choroid. Opacity in Glaucoma best seen
when we look directly into pupil, & is appears in a
gt. measure or altogether when we look sideways on
eye. In cataract, the opacity is seen whether we
look sideways or directly.

► , I believe it may any generally ,
× glaucoma, for in the advanced stage the centre of the
post.- lamellae of the lens is of a reddish-brown colour

× P:
om
to i

► in the posterior half of the lens, or

► transparent ring.

A page from William Mackenzie's specially printed copy of his *Treatise* with blank
pages interleaved for notes for future editions 1830. These notes were on the subject
of glaucoma, a condition which puzzled Mackenzie and is still puzzling his succes-
sors. In these notes he is enlarging on his observations on the 'Green Cataract'. The
first note advises examiners to look directly into the pupil to observe it properly. In

pupil presents the jet-black colour of health. The appearance, however, is not so much an actual opacity, as a paleness, or greenishness, discerned only when the eye is regarded in certain directions, and which we know to be the result of the light being reflected from a diseased choroid. ✗ This symptom is what we now term *glaucoma*, which has by mistake been commonly attributed to opacity of the vitreous humour. Repeated dissections of the eye in the state of glaucoma have convinced me, that deficiency of the pigmentum nigrum is the cause of this symptom, which is often attended, no doubt, by dissolution of the hyaloid membrane, and sometimes by yellowness of the centre of the lens. *I am speaking of ...*

To distinguish incipient amaurosis with glaucoma, from incipient cataract, proves to beginners one of the most difficult pieces of diagnosis, and sometimes not to beginners only, but to those who for a length of time have attended to the diseases of the eye. About ten years ago, a gentleman was sent to me by his brother, a medical practitioner in the country, desirous to know if I thought the cataracts, which he said I would see in his eyes, were ready for operation. The disease was glaucoma, with a great degree of shortness of sight, but without (any disease of the lens.) With much difficulty could I convince the brother of the real nature of the case, so wedded was he to the opinion that the opacity which he saw through the pupil, was cataract. The eyes of this patient continue at this day very nearly in the same state. I could mention many similar cases.

Attention to the following circumstances, will in general enable the careful observer to discriminate between glaucomatous amaurosis and cataract.

First, The opacity in glaucoma is always greenish, whereas, in incipient cataract, it is greyish, *or milk & water colour.*

Secondly, In glaucoma, the opacity appears to be seated at a considerable distance behind the pupil, or even deep in the vitreous humour; whereas, in lenticular cataract, it is evident that the opacity is close behind the pupil. In posterior capsular cataract, the opacity is deep in the eye, but is always streaked; whereas, the glaucomatous reflection is always uniform, never spotted, nor radiated, *& always uniform ...*

Thirdly, When we examine narrowly the surface of a lenticular opacity, especially while concentrating the light upon it by means of a double-convex lens, it is seen to be slightly rough, and somewhat dull, never smooth or polished, in these respects forming a striking contrast to the appearances pre-

taract, he writes, the opacity is seen 'whether we look sideways or directly'. In the third note, he describes the reddish-brown colour of the lens in the advanced stages of glaucoma as opposed to the above description in incipient glaucoma.

produced by kind permission of the Council of the Royal Society of Medicine, London.

him as affectionate, gay and even jovial with a clear intelligent brain to the end. Mathematics, he thought, was Mackenzie's least talent and others would agree that his book on the Physiology of Vision was not his best.

George Rainy stressed how rare it was to find a combination of great professional learning, critical acumen, great practical experience and sagacity, but all these Mackenzie possessed and enabled him to produce his *Treatise* when he had not yet reached the age of forty, was still engaged in general practice and still lecturing on a variety of subjects. Rainy summed up his contribution to Ophthalmology thus; 'If Dr Mackenzie did not effect any great revolution in ophthalmology, there can be no doubt that the publication of his work marks an epoch in the history of the science, for, till then, there was no equally comprehensive treatise on the subject, embodying the knowledge of the first third of the century.' Rainy also remarks on Mackenzie's very retentive memory, but also on his note-taking, which he did in private practice and also at the Eye Infirmary. He describes him as a cool deliberate operator with a strong dislike of all affectation of dash or brilliance. He was, he said, opposed to the operation for squint and also to iridectomy for glaucoma, but in both cases he reconsidered and practised them enthusiastically.

Rainy was not unconscious of Mackenzie's failings. He was, he said, sometimes lacking in a sense of the respect due to the professional distinction of others and, on occasions, laid about him without much respect of persons, nor did he suffer the eminence of an antagonist to blunt the edge of his sarcasm. Thus, offence was probably given in some cases where none was meant.

Rainy agreed with Warlomont that he was genial and pleasant and wrote that he had an inexhaustible fund of quaint humour and amusing anecdotes which made him a most entertaining companion. His reminiscences of Glasgow extended over seventy years and his accurate memory enabled him to recall the characters of former days very vividly. These included the medical celebrities of London and the Continent, of course.

George Rainy concludes, 'It would, perhaps, be premature to speculate as to the place which Mackenzie's name will ultimately occupy in the history of ophthalmology. In the field of discovery and original research it must yield precedence to others. But in arranging and systematizing what was already known, in contributing throughout a long life the most valuable additions to the general stock of information, and in bringing erudition to bear on the discussion of every branch of the subject, he has rendered a service which can hardly be over-estimated.'

Freeland Fergus recalled two other facts about Mackenzie in addition to details similar to those recorded by Warlomont and Rainy. Firstly, he recorded the story of the small fees he charged. Secondly, he wrote that Mackenzie was known in Glasgow and the West of Scotland for his lotion which, he said, was practically a solution of sal alembroth. It was, in fact, described in Martindale and Westcott's book in 1932 as a lotion composed of corrosive sublimate, ammonium chloride, belladonna extract, cochineal and proof spirit. Corrosive sublimate was one of the best antiseptics in Mackenzie's time when mercury in many forms was used for a great variety of ailments. Lotions are not used very much now by the ophthalmologist and Mackenzie's lotion is but a memory.

There is little to add to these estimates of his character. Those who wrote about him seemed surprised, as they might well have been, that he under-estimated the value of the ophthalmoscope. It is a strange coincidence that the motto of the Earls of Seaforth, ancient Chiefs of Clan Mackenzie was 'Luceo non uro' – 'I shine. I do not burn'. What a splendid motto for the ophthalmoscope and how strange that such an illustrious member of the clan should have been so hesitant about using an instrument which did so much to illuminate literally and metaphorically the study of diseases of the eye! But he came round to it just as he did to tenotomy for squints and to iridectomy for glaucoma.

This then is the story of a wee Glasgow man who accepted the challenge of his day. When he was born, the art of healing was just beginning to throw off the shackles of mediaeval mysticism and false ideas. The time was ripe for intellignet men to bring scientific knowledge to bear on the subject. Slowly thoughts were added to theories and the new scientific age of medicine was born and grew. This knowledge, however, had to be made available to everybody and it was here that William Mackenzie made his name. He founded an Eye Infirmary where students and doctors could learn about diseases of the eye and he lectured to them. He wrote a book which Hirschberg of Berlin described as 'The first English Text Book of Ophthalmology which belongs to the literature of the World' and which was deemed worthy of translation into French, German and Italian and of publication in the United States of America.

George Rainy was not quite certain what place he would occupy in the history of Ophthalmology, but history has passed judgment and he is assured of immortality in the ranks of those who served their fellow-men so faithfully in the building up of the specialty.

We who come after salute his memory.

Index